*PERGAMON INTERNATIONAL
POPULAR SCIENCE SERIES*

MOON IN FOCUS

KU-113-478

MOON IN FOCUS

BY

THOMAS RACKHAM

1966
THE QUEEN'S AWARD
TO INDUSTRY 1966

PERGAMON PRESS

OXFORD · LONDON · EDINBURGH · NEW YORK

TORONTO · SYDNEY · PARIS · BRAUNSCHWEIG

PERGAMON PRESS LTD.,
Headington Hill Hall, Oxford
4 & 5 Fitzroy Square, London, W.1

PERGAMON PRESS (SCOTLAND) LTD.,
2 & 3 Teviot Place, Edinburgh 1

PERGAMON PRESS INC.,
44–01 21st Street, Long Island City, New York 11101

PERGAMON OF CANADA LTD.,
6 Adelaide Street East, Toronto, Ontario

PERGAMON PRESS (AUST.) PTY. LTD.,
Rushcutters Bay, Sydney, New South Wales

PERGAMON PRESS S.A.R.L.,
24 rue des Écoles, Paris 5e

VIEWEG & SOHN GmbH,
Burgplatz 1, Braunschweig

First Edition 1968 PERGAMON INTERNATIONAL
POPULAR SCIENCE SERIES
Library of Congress Catalog Card No. 67–28655

Printed in Great Britain by A. Wheaton & Co., Ltd, Exeter

08 003458 6 (Flexicover)
08 003794 1 (hard cover

To Stella

Contents

List of Figures

List of Plates

Acknowledgements

I AM very grateful indeed to all the kindly folk who helped me to write this book.

First on the list comes the name of Ing. Antonín Rükl of Prague, Czechoslovakia, who spent many wearying and eye-straining hours in the production of the fine 1:10-million scale chart of the Moon. The fact that he succeeded in composing a line-diagram containing all of the larger lunar features, while still preserving the telescopic appearance of the lunar disc, leads me to suppose that some of the magic of the old alchemists still pervades the narrow, cobbled and stone-stepped streets of the Malá Strana.

Secondly, I offer my thanks to Professor Z. Kopal, Head of the Department of Astronomy in the University of Manchester, who gave me encouragement and allowed me to use lunar photography from our departmental archives.

Thirdly, to the United States National Aeronautical and Space Administration and in particular to the Jet Propulsion Laboratory, California Institute of Technology, who built and flew the Rangers, I owe a debt of thanks for the use of a few frames from the Ranger 9 photography.

My wife and daughter helped me to type the original manuscript and, between them, they compiled the list of named lunar features and their selenographic positions. It is almost certain that they did not get thanked at the conclusion of these tasks so I am taking the opportunity of doing it here in black and white.

I would also like to acknowledge the assistance of Mr. Charles Lowe for his help in the design of the cover for this book.

Lastly, I am grateful to my publishers who patiently awaited a manuscript that was long overdue by the time it arrived in Oxford.

CHAPTER 1

The Moon

ANY author who attempts to discuss the Moon must try to describe an object that is both familiar and strange to his readers. Familiar in the sense that, to most people gifted with reasonable eyesight, it is a symbol of the night and a "light to lighten the darkness" of those whose nightly wanderings take them away from the glare of sodium and neon. It is also a light that excites little comment when it is seen in the sky, and it is seldom missed when it is not there, unless it be by the eternal suitor. In what sense, then, can such a familiar object be strange? In the chapters that follow we shall verbally discard the "distance" that has lent so much enchantment to the Moon over the centuries, and unveil some of its mysteries, marvel at its wonders, and perhaps try to anticipate the surprises that lie in store for the first lunar explorers.

Before commencing this voyage of discovery it would be interesting to review briefly, and by no means exhaustively, some of the odd and learned notions that were held about the Moon by the early astronomers, and, since astronomy is the oldest of the sciences, this takes us back to the dawn of recorded history. Long before this, in prehistoric times, the Moon must have provided a mysterious and necessary light for our cave-dwelling ancestors, for without it the nocturnal hunter could not seek and kill his sleeping prey, and the Moon's absence, due to persistent clouds, may well have been a life-or-death affair for isolated communities. Small wonder then that it was deified and venerated as a source of light thousands of years ago; but this is not all, the Moon was also recognized prehistorically as a celestial timekeeper—a natural calendar by which the vitally important seasons of seedtime and harvest could be gauged, and it is no phonetical coincidence that associates the modern words "Moon" and "month".

Most of the fragmentary evidence that survives from the earliest astronomical records, dating from approximately 4000 B.C., seems generally to substantiate the view that most of the early Chinese, Egyptian and Babylonian astronomers were occupied with the motions, distances and eclipses of the Sun and Moon rather than with the physical natures of the two bodies. This is in no way surprising, for, to them, the invention of the telescope was in the remote future, and without optical aid it is impossible to study the physical structure of the Moon. However, the records indicate that restless and enquiring astronomical minds pondered these enigmas. Thales of Miletus, a Greek astronomer who lived some 600 years before Christ, believed that the Sun, Moon and stars were solid bodies—which at any rate is true of the Moon—and pronounced accurately that the Moon shone only by the Sun's reflected light. How influential a tutor Thales was history does not record, but his views on this subject do not seem to have made a lasting impression on one of his pupils, Anaximander, who pictured the Moon as a hollow rim of a wheel filled with a luminous substance, and to explain the ever-varying apparent shapes or phases he invoked an additional agency to open and close the aperture of the wheel. This theory was somewhat similar to one postulated by Heraclitus of Ephesus who announced, about one century later, that the Moon was a bowl of fire! Eclipses, and presumably phase conditions too, were caused by the sides of the bowl coming between the terrestrial observer and the fire. The originators of such unlikely mechanisms relied heavily on complicated props and devices to buttress their ideas, but all of these flimsy edifices eventually collapsed and were swept away on the floodtide of knowledge. They are worth recalling, nevertheless, for they show the gropings of erudite men for the truth, and for this their memories should be respected.

Closely following Heraclitus came Democritus, who asserted correctly that the Moon was a world having both mountains and valleys similar to those on the Earth, and Anaxagoras, a contemporary of Democritus, also takes credit for realizing the true nature of solar and lunar eclipses.

A few years later, around 350 B.C., the great philosopher Aristotle is known to have subscribed to the belief that the Moon was a sphere, and astronomers applaud him for his discovery of the real nature of the lunar phases which we shall examine in a later chapter. Whereas, up to his time, most astronomers regarded the Earth as a flat object—a belief which continued to hold considerable sway until the fourteenth and fifteenth centuries A.D.—Aristotle asserted that the Earth was a sphere, because he had seen its circular shadow crossing and darkening the lunar disc during times of eclipse.

Other famous names clamour for attention, among them Aristarchus of Samos, Hipparchus of Nicea, and the great Ptolemy, who measured the distance of the Moon by methods that are still in use today, and we could go on at some length discussing and examining the theories of the classical astronomers. However, by doing this, we should be merely recalling echoes from an adequately recorded past, and we should by-pass the purpose of the present volume.

Through ancient and medieval times the Moon was an indispensable adjunct to everyday life; both scholar and peasant knew full well that 30 days, as measured by the successive risings of the Sun, were just long enough for the Moon to complete a full set of phases. Neither were they in danger of forgetting that twelve successive "moonths" constituted a span of sufficient duration to contain a whole seasonal cycle consisting of Winter, Spring, Summer and Autumn.

It is against this inherited background, intertwined as it is with folklore and superstition, that we review the present position. Denizens of modern communities have little use for lunar calendars: mechanical clocks and electronic timekeepers have for ever ousted the Moon, the sundial and the hour-glass, and it is a little disturbing to discover that modern man, in some ways, tends to know less about lunar matters than did his forefathers. On the other hand, this statement is not altogether true, for he also lives under a verbal barrage generated by what might be loosely termed the "Space Age", and he cannot fail to be influenced by this, or respond to some of its more vociferous pronouncements that reach him by the various media of radio, television and the Press. It is often said that the Press has conditioned itself to provide the type of fare that its readers demand, and, if the size of the letters forming the headlines bears any relationship to the upward movement of surprised eyebrows, then we have already accepted rocket-borne satellites as part of our everyday experience. Moon-shots, if successful, like the recent Ranger and Lunik series, still "make the headlines", but these are only "nine-day wonders" and it seems that we are heading towards a technological era in which man's achievements will far outweigh his capacity to marvel at them. This is why we, in the 1960's, are the most fortunate population of all time, for we can still anticipate fantastic events, including manned lunar landings within the next few years. The dream, of men equipped to escape the gravitational bonds of the earth and voyage towards distant spheres, that has excited the minds of philosophers throughout the ages, will soon be reality. A few more ticks on the cosmic clock will translate fiction into fact, and man will step out of his space-craft and walk upon the surface of the Moon. What better excuse than this do we need to continue our study of that unique world?

CHAPTER 2

The Moon in Space

ON ANY cloudless night an upturned glance will bring into view
myriads of bright points of light that we know better as stars. If
we select any one of them at random and start to travel towards it
in the fleetest and most manoeuvrable of all space vehicles—our
imagination—we can traverse the inconceivably vast abysses of
space in a few seconds to arrive hare-like in the vicinity of our
chosen star. So unimaginable are the distances involved that tor-
toise-like light, travelling at a mere 186,000 miles per second,
would take a few decades to complete the same journey. A closer
examination of our star would reveal that it was no longer a point,
but a dazzling disc of light, evidently the visible face of a vast and
blinding sphere of light and heat. It is no coincidence that this
shining orb reminds us of our Sun, and it would not have changed
anything very much had we chosen to visit any other star in the
sky, for all stars are suns. Some, like Antares and Betelgeuse, are
very much larger, while others are smaller than our own Sun,
which happens to be a fairly average type of star.

Let us assume that the star we have visited is our Sun—it is
very easy to get lost in space—and let us stop at a point in space
where its disc subtends an angle of about half a degree, which is
how we see it from the Earth. With luck and quite close to us we
might possibly be able to discern two small dark spheres that are
made visible by the Sun's light shining on them. The larger sphere
is about four times the diameter of the smaller, and the distance
between them is thirty times the diameter of the larger body. If we
watch them long enough—time is no barrier in the realm of
imagination—we shall see that they are travelling companions

in space. By speeding up their movements we shall discover that when the larger body has made one complete orbit, or path, around the Sun, the smaller sphere has described no less than twelve smaller circles around the larger. This means that sometimes the three bodies are almost in line, with the smaller in between, and, at other times, the smaller sphere occupies the outside position. To make matters a little clearer we can invoke a mechanical analogy: imagine two flat multi-toothed gear-wheels that can be meshed together. The larger is fixed by a central screw to a flat horizontal surface so that the smaller wheel can be meshed with it in such a way as to enable it to move freely in either direction around the periphery of the larger wheel. If this is done experimentally, some difficulty may be found in keeping the smaller wheel in mesh, but, for the purposes of this discussion, we can assume that this problem has been solved. The smaller wheel will undoubtedly have a hole in its centre, and additionally we can put a dot of paint near the edge of this wheel, close to the gear teeth. As the smaller wheel is rotated it will pull itself, by its teeth, round the periphery of the larger fixed wheel, and the following things will be observed. Firstly, the centres of the two wheels will remain the same distance apart all the time. Secondly, the paint dot will keep revolving around the centre of the smaller wheel, so that its distance from the centre of the larger wheel will vary continuously between the limits set by the linear distance of the wheel centres plus or minus the radius of the paint spot from the centre of the smaller wheel. With a little mechanical skill we could add spheres to this model (see Fig. 1), and the largest, that we place in the middle of the larger wheel, would represent the Sun, while, above the centre of the smaller wheel, we could place a tiny Earth; and an even smaller sphere could be fixed above the paint spot to represent the Moon. In such a model or orrery it would be impossible to make everything to the correct scale and this would mask the fact that, despite its almost circular path around the Earth, the Moon nevertheless possesses a solar orbit in which the distances are so vast and the curvatures so slight that at all times its path may be described as "concave" to the Sun. In a similar

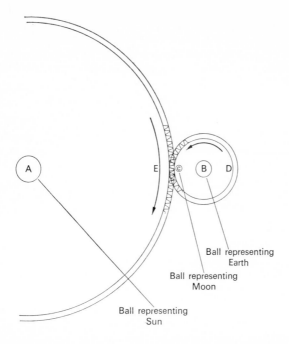

Fig. 1. D and E are the smaller and larger tooth gear-wheels respectively. A is a ball fixed to the centre of E to represent the Sun. B, a second ball fixed at the centre of D, represents the Earth. C, the smallest ball fixed to a point near the periphery of D represents the Moon. The rotation of D will move it round the periphery of E, and C will rotate round B. At the same time the distance between A and B remains constant, but the distance of A and C will vary between the limits of the distance AB plus or minus BC.

way the line of any circle may be described as "concave" to the point at its centre. Having taken this external view of the Sun–Earth–Moon system we can appreciate some of the difficulties of the ancient astronomers who attempted to interpret celestial movements from a vantage-point of a "fixed" Earth around which the Sun, Moon and planets were supposed to revolve.

We have seen how our Sun is just an ordinary star, and it is no more prodigal in its output of light and heat than any other average star. Fortunately we inhabit a planet that happens at this epoch to be correctly placed to receive the benefits of the solar radiations. Some idea of how much closer we are to the Sun than to any other star can be gauged from the fact that light from the Sun takes 8 minutes to reach us, whereas light from the nearest star is more than 4 years old by the time it impinges on the Earth. In this age of TV advertising, every commodity is "new" or "instant", but neither of these adjectives could be used for the marketing of star-light!

The Solar System

Before we proceed to discuss dimensions and distances, we ought to make brief mention of the Solar System. There are 9 planets that form the more important members of the Solar System; in order of increasing distance from the Sun these are: Mercury, Venus, Earth, Mars, Jupiter, Saturn, Uranus, Neptune and Pluto. Of these Jupiter is the largest—no less than 1000 Earths could be placed within its giant volume—and Mercury is the fleetest and smallest, being rather less than half the diameter of the Earth. All the planets describe elliptical orbits about their primary, the Sun, and these orbits occupy a fairly flat plane in space, rather like the flat plane that surrounds the hole in a gramophone record. To paint a few spots on the gramophone record at various distances from the hole, to represent the planets, would serve no useful purpose, however, since this would imply that all were completing orbits simultaneously, for one turn of the record would result in all spots making complete turns. With the planets, the farther the body is away from the Sun the longer it will take to complete an orbit; for example, Mercury hurtles round the Sun in 88 days, while Pluto, as if starved of light and heat, crawls round once every 246 years!

As was remarked earlier, most people today are familiar with Earth's artificial satellites, and this book is dedicated to a survey of the Earth's only natural satellite, the Moon. Perhaps remaining doubts will be dispelled if we note that planets are no more or less than satellites of the Sun. So, to sum up, a planet encircles the Sun and takes with it, perhaps as in the case of Jupiter, a whole family of satellites, each member making its individual orbit about its parent planet.

The Lunar Orbit and Librations

If we wish to be precise, we should say that the Earth and Moon rotate about their common centre of gravity, and we can imagine the type of configuration that would have resulted from both bodies being of equal mass. Tie a string around the centre of the handle of a dumb-bell and let it hang freely in space and the weighted ends will rotate about the centre of the handle. In the case of the Earth–Moon system the "dumb-bell" is very unbalanced and, since the mass of the Moon is rather less than one-eighteenth of the Earth's, their centre of gravity is actually within the Earth's sphere; thus it is quite true to say that the Moon revolves round the Earth.

Now for a few facts and figures (see also tabulated data in the Appendix). The Sun is a gigantic orb of nearly 865,000 miles in diameter, and it is small wonder that the 7900-mile-diameter Earth maintains a respectful average of 92·9 million miles from this vast nuclear power-house.

The Moon, with a diameter of 2160 miles, describes an elliptical orbit that brings it, at its closest, to within 226,426 miles of the Earth's centre. This is called *perigee*, and the Moon's angular diameter as seen by an observer on the terrestrial surface is then 33′ 31″—written 33 minutes and 31 seconds of arc. It is as well to note that these minutes and seconds have nothing to do with time, although there is some superficial resemblance in that one minute is one-sixtieth of one degree, and one second is one-sixtieth of a minute of arc. When astronomers discuss very small angles in the sky they frequently use the unit of one-tenth of a second of arc.

At *apogee*, when the Moon is farthest from us, the total mileage is 252,731 and the apparent angular diameter also decreases in the ratio of about 8:7 to yield a disc diameter of 29′ 23″. These are the two extremes, and a good deal of the time the perigee diameters are smaller than that quoted above, while the apogee diameters

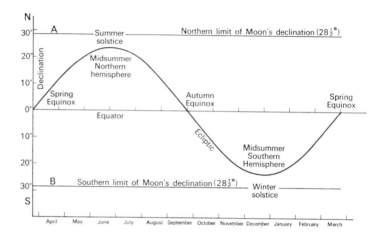

FIG. 2. The curved path of the Sun called the ecliptic is plotted here for a period of 1 year. Angles of declination are identical to terrestrial latitude. It is not possible to plot the Moon's motions because these are variable, and there would be twelve of them to insert in this figure. This figure represents a mercator projection of the complete sky up to plus and minus 30° declination. The upper and lower limits of the Moon's motions are shown by the lines A and B. Thus the Moon will always be found plus or minus 28½° of the equator (see also Fig. 3).

are often larger than 29′ 23″. Most of the time, when the Moon is discussed in general terms, we prefer to use the mean or average distance which has recently been determined very accurately by radar. Corrected to give the distance between the centres of the two bodies, this measurement yields a value of 238, 857 ± 1 miles which is equivalent to an angular diameter of 31′ 05″·3. When we have to deal with cosmic distances that are less than about one million miles, we can readily appreciate that the Moon is a very small and parochial object indeed, and only appears to be the same size as the Sun because it is 400 times closer to us.

The standard reference plane for the Solar System is the *ecliptic*, which is defined as the apparent path of the Sun as seen against the backcloth of distant and what appear to be "fixed" stars.

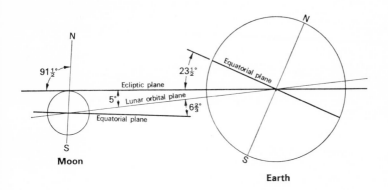

FIG. 3. The ecliptic is the plane of the Earth's orbit around the Sun. The Earth's equatorial plane is tilted at an angle of about $23\frac{1}{2}°$ to the ecliptic and, since the lunar orbital plane is inclined a little more than 5° to the ecliptic, it can be seen that the Moon can be overhead in latitudes of plus or minus $28\frac{1}{2}°$ at certain times of year. The lunar equatorial plane is tilted at $1\frac{1}{2}°$ to the ecliptic and at nearly 7° to the lunar orbital plane (see librations in latitude).

"Apparent" in this sense means how the phenomenon appears to the beholder: actually it is we who are rotating about the Sun and, to a hypothetical observer on the Sun, it would be the Earth that were changing its position against the background of fixed stars. The ecliptic is not to be confused with the Earth's equatorial plane (see Fig. 2) for this would imply that the Sun would appear to be overhead on the equator all the year round, and this is noticeably not the case. If it were, there would be no seasons, and the risings and settings of the Sun would occur at fixed times for any given terrestrial location. Also our luminary would appear and disappear at the same points on the horizon every day and its highest altitude at midday above a chosen horizon would ever be the same.

The terrestrial equatorial plane is inclined at an angle of almost $23\frac{1}{2}°$ to the ecliptic, which is considerably more than the inclination of the *lunar equatorial plane*—a mere $1\frac{1}{2}°$ (see Fig. 3). *The lunar orbital plane* around the Earth is inclined to the ecliptic by a little more than $5°$ and this is an important angle for the astronomer for, at certain times, the Moon can be seen at the zenith, that is, exactly overhead, in latitudes $28\frac{1}{2}°$ north or south of the equator.

The lunar equatorial plane is also tilted at an angle of nearly $7°$ to the lunar orbital plane, in other words, the lunar axis of rotation, which is the axis that passes through the lunar north and south poles and about which the Moon turns in space, is inclined to the orbital plane. By this means both north and south poles are alternately inclined towards the Earth, and observations can be made of lunar areas that are otherwise hidden from terrestrial view. This "nodding" of the "man in the Moon's head" is called the *libration in latitude*.

There is another libration—the *libration in longitude*—and this permits us to see a little of the normally hidden east and west limbs of the Moon.

To understand the causes of the librations in longitude we require to know a little more about the Moon's movements in space. Firstly, let us consider the lunar axial rotation, which is constant and has been measured accurately and found to be $29 \cdot 531$ days. That is to say, the Moon, spinning like a ponderous top, makes one revolution per month. And since this is just the length of time required for the Moon to complete one orbit round the Earth, it may not, at first, be apparent as to how the librations in longitude occur. It can be said at once that if the lunar orbit were perfectly circular such phenomena could not occur; these librations are entirely due to the elliptical shape of the lunar orbit; thus it would not be amiss at this point to examine some of the properties of ellipses.

A few years ago Western countries were swept by the "hula-hoop" craze, and young people everywhere were seen practising the necessary circumvolutions to keep the hoops rotating about their bodies. If we look at such a hoop we should expect it to be approximately circular in shape, but by exerting some pressure upon it we could make it into an ellipse: moreover, by altering the pressure we could make any number of ellipses. The poor "hula hoop" would be in pieces long before we could extend our family of ellipses to include the very eccentric or flattened ones. Since all our flattened circles are called ellipses, and since they are obviously

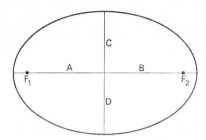

Fig. 4. In the ellipse the lengths A plus B constitute the major axis —each is a semi-major axis. Semi-minor axes, C and D, together likewise form the minor axis. F_1 and F_2 are the foci of the ellipse. In the Earth–Moon system the Earth is located at one of the foci.

not of the same shape, we must find some way of defining the degree of ellipticity. A convenient shape to consider is the plan view of a ship's life-boat; it is true that it is not quite an ellipse because of the pointed bow and stern, but even these are useful because they indicate the linear extremities of the boat. On our plan if we were to connect these two points by a single straight line, we could call this line the major axis of the boat. Round off the points and this line would become the major axis of an ellipse. Using the boat analogy the minor axis is the line drawn at right angles to the major axis through the widest section half-way along the boat: the minor axis of an ellipse is similarly defined (see Fig. 4).

Now we must bring in two important items that have not yet been mentioned: these are the two foci without which it would be impossible to construct an ellipse by the time-honoured pins–pencil–string method. Depending on the degree of eccentricity, the foci are to be found on the line of the major axis and at equal distances from the central point where the minor axis bisects it. Thus, the eccentricity of an ellipse is the ratio of the distance between the two foci and the length of the major axis, but astronomers frequently prefer to use only half an ellipse. Let us take the distances given earlier and work out the eccentricity of the lunar orbit. First add the perigee and apogee distances together to find the major axis:

$$226,426 + 252,731 = 479,157 \text{ miles.}$$

To get the *semi*-major axis we divide this distance by 2.

$$\frac{479,157}{2} = 239,578 \text{ miles.}$$

Subtract the perigee distance to determine the distance of one of the foci from the central point of the major axis:

$$239,578 - 226,426 = 13,152 \text{ miles.}$$

$$\text{Eccentricity} = \frac{\text{Focal distance from centre}}{\text{Semi-major axis}}$$

$$= \frac{13,152}{239,578} = 0 \cdot 055.$$

The eccentricity of the lunar orbit is not very great, yet it is enough to cause the librations in longitude, and the explanation stems from Kepler's second law which states that the line or vector that joins the Earth to the Moon marks out equal areas (of our ellipse) in equal times. At perigee this line is at its shortest, and therefore it has to move swiftly at this time and cuts out a wide, though short, wedge. At apogee, the radial velocity of the line is reduced so that our orbital slices are long and narrow. In the same way the Moon accelerates and slows down according to its orbital position. However, let us first consider what would happen if the Moon's orbit were truly circular with a zero eccentricity. This would bring the two foci together in a point at the gravitational centre, and the lunar orbital speed would be constant. Since, as we have already noted, the axial rotation of the Moon is exactly the same as its orbital period, an observer would find, ignoring all other disturbing influences, that a defined point in the centre of the lunar disc would always keep in the centre no matter where the Moon was in its orbit. With an eccentric orbit, we no longer have this happy state of affairs, and the constant axial rotation tends to get a little out of phase with the orbital period owing to the changing lunar velocity. To the terrestrial observer this means that he can see, alternately, a little more of the lunar surface beyond the normal eastern and western limbs (see Fig. 5).

As well as the *optical librations*, which is the correct term for the phenomena that we have been reviewing, and which cause apparent displacements of $\pm 7\cdot 6°$ in longitude and $\pm 6\cdot 7°$ in latitude, there are physical librations amounting to $\pm 0\cdot 02°$ in longitude and $\pm 0\cdot 04°$ in latitude caused by irregularities in the axial rotation of the Moon. The latter, however, are long-term effects whose influences are of academic interest to astronomers, who spend much of their time seeking to learn more and more about less and less.

Before leaving the subject of the librations, there is one other that allows the terrestrial observer to see a little more of the lunar surface, although these advantages are usually more than offset by disadvantages. We refer here to the *diurnal libration* which is due to the Earth's axial rotation that takes the observer along with it. We can get the same effect on a much smaller scale on the fairground, where we can board the big vertical wheel with the swinging seats that carries us 50 feet or so above the ground. If we suppose that the fairground is built on the beach of a seaside resort, we can take our seat in the wheel a few feet above sea-level. For the sake of argument, let us choose the height of 6 feet, and our horizon on the sea will be only $2\cdot 6$ nautical miles away. As the wheel rotates our height will increase and so will the distance

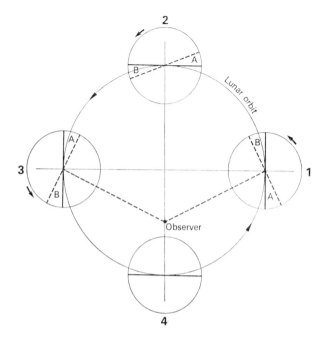

Fig. 5. Librations in longitude are caused by the loss of synchro-
nism between the Moon's constant axial rotation and its variable
orbital velocity. The diagram cannot be drawn to scale, but the effect
can be understood if we move the observer away from the centre. At
position 1 the broken line indicates the hemispherical boundary;
the unbroken line indicates the hemisphere visible under synchronous
conditions. To the observer area A becomes visible; B is hidden. At
position 2, A is hidden and B is visible—this condition is called
"mean" libration in longitude. At position 3, A is hidden and area
B is visible. Position 4 gives a view similar to that of position 2.

of the horizon, until at 50 feet we shall be able to see small craft
7·5 nautical miles distant. In a similar manner we can extend our
view of the lunar horizon by riding "up to the top" or "down to
the bottom" of the gigantic 8000-mile-diameter "wheel" that we
inhabit, for it is at the centre of the "wheel" where we get none of

these advantages (see Fig. 6). Imagine a straight line joining the centres of the Earth and Moon. An observer standing at the point where the straight line pierces the Earth's crust would not be well placed for viewing extensions of the lunar limbs, but other observers standing 4000 miles east or west of him would see setting and rising Moons respectively near their horizons. To observers who are favourably situated in the manner described, the setting Moon shows a little more of its western limb, and where

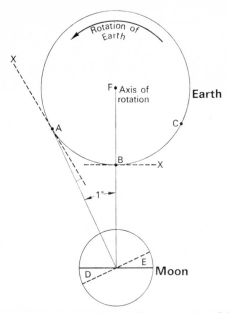

Fig. 6. The diurnal libration is caused by the rotation of the Earth. In the diagram, A represents the position of an observer with the Moon low on his horizon, X. The border of the lunar hemisphere seen under this condition is shown as the broken line. Area D is seen and E is invisible. The Earth rotating about axis F in a few hours brings the observer to position B thus changing his angle of view by about 1°. He is now permitted to see the hemisphere bordered by the unbroken line: area E is now visible and area D is no longer visible. A similar phenomenon occurs when the Moon is setting and the observer's position has rotated to C. The diagram greatly exaggerates the effect.

it is rising displays a little more of its eastern limb—east and west as used here are defined in the same way as directions on Earth. The disadvantages that were referred to earlier stem, usually, from the bad observing conditions caused by viewing the Moon low down in the sky at moonrise or moonset: in fact, the observer often sacrifices the librational effects so as to enjoy the satisfaction of seeing the Moon at, or near, the zenith when he is observing through the thinnest and least disturbed layer of the earth's atmosphere.

There is one other effect concerning rising and setting Moons that is worthy of mention. Taking moonrise only, the observer who sees the Moon coming up over his horizon is "riding" the Earth quite swiftly in the direction of the Moon, and, as a consequence, our satellite rises quickly above the horizon. Six hours later, however, when the Moon is due south (or, in the southern hemisphere, due north) the path of the observer is at right angles to what it was at moonrise. Therefore the Moon's motion across the sky at this time is not so swift. At moonset the reverse conditions apply and the Moon drops below the horizon quite swiftly.

Taking the sum total of all librations, the Moon reveals to terrestrial observers no less than 59 % of its surface. The remaining 41 % has not yet been seen by human eye, but we do know what it looks like because the Russian Lunik 3, launched on 4th October, 1959, succeeded in relaying back to Earth photographs of about three-quarters of the hidden hemisphere taken at a distance of 37,000 to 43,000 miles from the Moon. This fantastic feat has been duplicated several times since and, even as I write, the American Lunar Orbiter,* a highly sophisticated instrument, is busily adding to our knowledge of the averted hemisphere. Just as 41 % has never been seen, so 82 % of the *hemisphere* facing us never disappears; but the Astronomical Ephemeris contains tabulated material that permits the astronomer to select the most favourable times to study the peripheral zones that are more favourably or adversely affected by the lunar librations each month.

* See note 1, p. 177.

Nowhere in the Universe can the astronomer or the cosmologist point to a body, or a volume of space, and assert that it is fixed or non-moving. This property of movement is to be found in the largest cosmic units as well as in the smallest far beyond the resolution of the most powerful of microscopes. By the same argument we cannot state that a given body possesses an absolute velocity, for all speeds are relative and cannot be measured at all unless they be compared to some other body that also has its individual velocity and direction in relation to something else. Thus we can speculate *ad infinitum*, and we can understand how the Moon revolves around the Earth and how the Earth makes its yearly orbit about the Sun. The Sun, undoubtedly, moves along in space and probably rotates about some fairly local star-cluster which, itself, moves as a unit round the Galaxy or Milky Way. Galaxies, too, hurtle at incredible velocities through the unimaginable and unending voids of the cosmos.

This seeming digression was included here merely to stress the large number of gravitational forces that are involved. The Earth, on account of its close proximity, and the Sun, because of its vast mass, are obviously the most important gravitational influences on the lunar orbit. The planets, too, conspire to perturb it, and even the deployment of the terrestrial continental land masses play their part. Nor must we forget the effect of the Earth's equatorial bulge. All of these things affect the lunar orbit to make it one of the most complicated motions known to astronomers.

The Lunar Phases

The *lunar phases* occur as a result of the Moon's orbital motions around the Earth, and to the naked-eye observer the phases are an endless source of interest, and we have already noted briefly that the erudite Aristotle is usually credited with the discovery of their true nature.

Actually the lunar phases are easier to understand than to explain. If a football is kicked on to a darkened road, and comes to rest in the centre of it in front of an approaching automobile, the car's headlights will illuminate the ball and show to the driver a complete hemisphere—a "full" football. A pedestrian approaching from the opposite direction will see nothing of the ball because, firstly, the hemisphere facing him is darkened and, secondly, he is also being dazzled by the headlamps of the car. This is exactly what happens with our lunar "football" and our "headlamp" the Sun. If the car stops with its lights still switched on, and if the pedestrian continues to walk along the side of the road, it is evident that he will begin to see some of the illuminated hemisphere of the football. This will first appear as a thin crescent and this will grow until exactly half a hemisphere is seen: this condition will occur when the pedestrian is just passing the ball, and when the angle formed between the headlights, the ball and the observer is a right angle. This could be called a "quarter" ball. Having passed the football the pedestrian will have to look back at it over his shoulder if he wishes to see it because it is now behind him. When he does so he sees more than half of the illuminated hemisphere, so, to him, the football presents what is called a "gibbous" phase. A similar, though mirror-image, apparition would result if our observer were to retrace his steps to the place where he first walked into our story, crossed the road and recommenced his walk from the opposite side. This time he would see in the "crescents" and "quarter" phases the other half of the illuminated hemisphere that had been invisible to him initially. Only when he gets past does the "gibbous" phased football reveal some of the illuminated area that had been visible to him from the opposite side of the road.

Now this explains exactly how the lunar phases appear, but it does not give an accurate account of *how* they occur. In order to do this we must exchange the positions of the pedestrian and the football, at the same time leaving the car plus its headlights where it is. We may imagine the football tied to a piece of cord in such a way as to permit the man in the middle of the road to whirl it round himself in a manner similar to that employed by a Scottish athlete throwing the hammer. By exercising our imagination we may slow this process down and then we can observe more closely the results of this experiment.

Putting ourselves in the position of the erstwhile pedestrian in the centre of the road, and flexing our muscles on the tethered football, we find that we can see nothing at all of the ball when it passes between us and the headlights. In the opposite direction, with the lights behind us, we can see a whole illuminated hemisphere such as was originally seen by the driver of the car. Half-way between these two positions there are two places where we can see half illuminated hemispheres. Starting again from the invisible "new" phase, we may witness, as the ball swings round us, increasing or *waxing* crescents up to "first quarter" and waxing "gibbous phases" up to the "full". After this we observe the same phenomena in reverse: the "full" *wanes* through the "gibbous phases" to "last quarter" and finally through ever-decreasing "crescents" to the invisible "new" or "old" phase lost in the glare of the car headlamps. Perhaps it is worth pointing out that the terms "new" and "old" have no real significance at the beginning or ending of a lunation: their main value is to furnish descriptions of the early and late crescent phases occurring just after sunset and just before sunrise respectively.

Retiring to a somewhat safer position than the middle of a darkened road, we can appreciate that the "football" phases we have just witnessed have exact parallels in their lunar counterparts. In a sense the Earth whirls a Moon, tethered by the invisible cord of gravitation, around itself in front of our headlight, the Sun. If we throw aside our "props" and "devices" we can easily see that the phases we have created are the same as those achieved naturally by the Moon every month. Thus the "new" or "old" Moon, by virtue of the conditions required to produce it, has always to be found in the same part of the sky as the Sun as seen from the Earth. The three bodies will be approximately in line for both the "new" and "full" phases, and it is apparent, if the "new" Moon occurs when that body comes between us and the Sun, that the "full" Moon takes place after our satellite has completed one-half or 180° of its orbit around the Earth. This half orbit takes 2 weeks to accomplish and, at the same time, removes the Moon from the midday skies to the midnight skies whence it rises at sunset and sets at sunrise after being visible all through the night.

The "quarters" that occur at the 90° and 270° positions in the lunar orbit can be seen only for about 6 hours in a darkened sky because at these times the Moon is only 90° away from the Sun. We can readily imagine this situation if we picture ourselves at sea with nothing to mar the symmetry of our horizons. The vault of heaven stretching from a point due east, through our zenith vertically above and down to a point due west of us, encompasses 180° or two right angles, and it is evident, if the Moon is at the zenith and separated from the Sun by 90°, that the latter is on the horizon and that the time of day is either sunrise or sunset. There is also no difficulty in showing that in both instances half of the Moon's journey across the sky is made in darkness and the other half in daylight.

The "crescents" are even less accessible for observation for, to obtain crescent phases, the Sun–Earth–Moon angle must be less than 90°. Also if the crescent Moons need to be observed in darkened skies much depends on the position of the observer on the Earth. For example, any place north of the Arctic Circle in the northern summer months would not be ideal, for, in June, in latitudes of 70° and more, there are occasions when the Sun and Moon are to be found close together in the sky for the whole 24 hours of the day. This means that the Moon would not be seen under ideal conditions required for the detailed study of the surface.

If we forsake this land of the "Midnight Sun", with its all too short summer, and head for the tropical regions of the Earth we find improved conditions for the detailed study of the crescent phases of the Moon. For here the Sun sets almost perpendicularly on the horizon and twilight is shorter in duration than it is in the more temperate latitudes and, as a result, the crescent Moon is often presented in a truly darkened sky. Similar phenomena occur also at sunrise. Despite these advantages observations require to be made quickly, for the Moon also rises and sets more vertically and quickly above tropical horizons.

Before leaving this important subject of the phases of the Moon let us quickly summarize what we have found out about them, and, in particular, when a specified phase can be seen. Let us start with the invisible "new Moon" that cannot be seen because the lunar surface turned towards us is completely darkened, and also because it occupies the same part of the sky as the Sun and is therefore lost in the glare of the daytime sky. Then, soon after sunset 2 or 3 days later, we see the waxing "crescent" phases of the "young" Moon and these grow from night to night as the angular separation between the Moon and the Sun increases as seen from the Earth. At an age of a little more than 7 days the Moon is at "first quarter" and the line of demarcation between the sunlit and darkened hemispheres then seems to be exactly straight to the terrestrial observer. This line is known as the *Morning Terminator* which may be described as one-half of the great circle defining the limits of the illuminated and unilluminated hemispheres. The other half of this great circle hidden behind the bulk of the Moon is called the *Evening Terminator*. Most of the time this great circle does not pass through the north and south lunar poles, like a meridian circle always passes through the terrestrial poles: this circle moves continually in relation to the lunar surface and does not pivot at any fixed point on this surface. It is nevertheless true that this circle always passes within a few degrees of the north and south lunar poles.

The morning terminator continues to move across the lunar globe until the whole hemisphere is visible at the "full"—this, as we have already noted, is best observed near the meridian of the observer at midnight when the Moon attains its highest altitude in the sky. At the same time it should be noted that it is very seldom indeed that one is fortunate enough to glimpse a Moon that is exactly "full" on one's meridian at midnight. Anyone intent upon making an earnest study of the lunar surface should try to make his telescopic observations when or near the time that the lunar orb crosses the local meridian, for then the observations may be conducted when atmospheric turbulence and absorption are least troublesome. Meridian observations can, of course, only be made on those phases that lie between "first" and "last" quarter. "Crescent" phases cannot be beneficially observed under these conditions.

After the "full" phase the Moon begins to wane and the morning terminator disappears from terrestrial gaze to continue its journey across the averted hemisphere. In its stead, and encroaching from the astronomical eastern edge of the visible hemisphere, comes the "evening terminator" that slowly and patiently whittles away ever-increasing slices of the lunar hemisphere until it, too, provides the Moon with a straight edge at "last quarter". Perhaps we ought to qualify the above statement by saying that it appears to whittle away ever-increasing slices because, although the terminators advance or retreat at the same rate, a 13° slice near the edge of the disc appears to be much thinner than one near the centre of the disc because of the globular foreshortening. The same effect causes circular lunar craters to appear elliptical near the limbs.

Following on from "last quarter" the last "crescent" phases of the "old Moon" occur closer and closer to sunrise each successive day and the extremely thin crescents are only visible for a few minutes before sunrise, and after this event they melt away and are lost in the wings of the morning close to the horizon.

So much then for the lunar phases that puzzled the ancient astronomers and for which they produced numerous and extravagant explanations.

Selenographic Coordinates

Astronomers have to be more exact than the layman in defining the positions of the lunar terminators and it is scarcely sufficient to say that the lunar phase is a little bit more than first quarter or a lot less than full. Neither can we attach much scientific value to an observation that was made when the Moon was shaped like a rugby ball or perhaps thin like a banana. Accordingly the Moon has been given a system of coordinates like those of the Earth and these are called the *selenographic coordinates* and they have their exact parallel in the geographical coordinates of the Earth with which most people are familiar. Thus there exists a prime lunar meridian and a lunar equator plus a full set of latitudes and longitudes.

With this system of coordinates it is possible to define exactly the position of the Sun or Earth in relation to the lunar surface by extending this system into space. It is easier to imagine this if we had a transparent Moon with the lines of selenographic latitude and longitude engraved round the outside of it. Furthermore, we could place a hypothetical observer exactly in the centre of such a sphere so that he would be able to see, not only the engraved coordinates, but also the Sun, Earth and any other of the celestial bodies he wished to observe. By peering at the centre of the solar disc at any instant of time he would be able to pin-point its position in relation to the lunar surface; and the numerical values of latitude and longitude that he would be able to assign to this point would also define that position on the lunar crust where he, the observer, would be able to stand in order to observe the Sun exactly overhead at his zenith.

Taking a terrestrial analogy, let us suppose that we have transported ourselves to the tropical regions of the Earth and that the Sun is at our zenith. This is midday for us, and before the evening darkness can overwhelm us we must wait for the Sun to set, or, to be more accurate, we must wait for the Earth to turn through an angle of 90°. Let us suppose that we are standing on the Greenwich meridian at noon, which implies that half the day is spent and that we still have the other half to look forward to. We might wonder where the Earth's morning and evening terminators were situated, for the Earth has terminators, too, like the Moon. It is obvious that the terminators must be 90° away from us at noontime and we can easily determine the places where sunrise and sunset are taking place. It so happens that the morning terminator of the Earth is passing across the central U.S.A., and the first warming rays of the Sun are helping to disperse the mists along the banks of the Mississippi River when it is noontime on the Greenwich meridian. Far to the east of us the evening terminator heralds nightfall on another mighty river—the Ganges in India.

So as to describe accurately the phase conditions of the Moon astronomers use the position of the morning terminator to define what is called the *Colongitude of the Sun*. Most of the time the lunar specialist is far more interested in the whereabouts of the morning or evening terminators than he is in the position of the subsolar point—the point on the lunar surface where the Sun is exactly overhead. Consequently it is the solar colongitude that is often tabulated in the ephemerides in preference to the selenographic longitude of the Sun. However, the difference can never amount to a greater or lesser amount than 90° so that the selenographic longitude can always be obtained by subtracting the value given for the colongitude from 90° or 450°. Thus we can construct without difficulty Table 1.

TABLE 1

Lunar phase	Colongitude of Sun (degrees)	Selenographic long. of Sun (degrees)
New Moon ⎱ Old Moon ⎰	270 or −90	180
First quarter	360 or 0	90
Full Moon	90	360 or 0
Last quarter	180	270 or −90

It is worth noting that longitudes between 90° and 270° are not visible from the Earth because they are on the averted lunar hemisphere: therefore the morning terminator disappears at full and does not reappear until after new Moon.

The author has no intention of elaborating further on the selenographic coordinates nor indeed on any other type of lunar coordinate systems, of which there are several. Nevertheless, it is useful to be able to remember, when we look at the inverted image of the Moon through an astronomical telescope, that longitude values increase as the eye scans from left to right and that the lunar central meridian has a numerical value of 360° or 0°.

Before leaving the subject of lunar coordinates there is a term that crops up from time to time that might usefully be explained at this point. Charts of the Moon are often constructed showing the disc at *mean libration*, which is a condition that can be approached but never satisfied from any point on the Earth's surface. In order to achieve this, all circles of lunar latitude seen edge-on must be drawn to appear as straight lines, and the Earth and the Moon are too close together in space to permit such a state of affairs to exist even if the circles of latitude were made visible by some miraculous means. Assuming that such lines were visible, the condition could be realized for, perhaps, the lunar equator, but all other lines of latitude would appear as curved lines. To be sure, somewhere in space at any instant of time, the Moon presents an aspect of mean libration, but these vantage-points are so far distant as to be completely useless to the selenographer.

The folded lunar chart at the end of this volume depicts the visible surface of the Moon at mean libration, and it also uses the selenographic coordinates with numerical values of +90 to −90 degrees in longitude.

Lunar Months

Most people—even astronomers—when asked to define a period of 1 month might find some difficulty in answering, for in a year there are seven months consisting of 31 days each; four of 30 days, while February has only 28 days except for its 4-yearly bonus of one extra day that it receives each leap year.

Another approach would be to divide the 365 days in the year into 12 equal months and this yields a figure of 30·4 days per month which, if adopted, would be somewhat cumbersome to control, for we should have to change the name of the month in question at a predetermined time during the day.

Returning from the ridiculous to the sublime subject of the Moon; most people might be astonished to learn that astronomers can define at least five different types of lunar months, although in all fairness we ought to add that four of these are periods that differ by only a few hours. From the restricted point of view of the denizens of the Earth, and bearing in mind how dependent are the feasts and fasts of, notably, the Islamic and other religions on the lunar phases, the most important period is the *synodical month*. This is the period of time that we have already used in our description of the lunar phases, and, because of this, no one ought to be surprised to learn that this type of month, consisting of 29·531 days, is measured from one new Moon to the next.

All of the remaining types of months are about 2 days shorter in duration and this requires a little explanation, as well as an introduction to the *sidereal period or month*. The adjectival term "sidereal" refers the phenomenon involved to the background of the fixed stars. Thus a sidereal day is the period of time that the Earth requires to rotate on its axis so that a given star comes back to a definable position above the observer's horizon. For example, a star could easily be observed immediately above a church spire by an observer standing on an identifiable spot a few hundred yards away from the spire. The next night the same observation could be made again from the same spot and against the same spire and, if the two passages of the star above the spire were carefully timed, the length of the sidereal or star day would be found to be 23 hours 56 minutes—4 minutes shorter than the "solar" day. The reason for this difference is to be found in the movement of the Earth around the Sun that demands that rather more than one complete rotation of the Earth must be made if the observer's point on the Earth's surface is going to be brought back into line with the vector joining the centres of the two bodies. The explanation is that the Earth has travelled along in its orbit around the Sun and has had to rotate an additional angular degree—equivalent of 4 minutes of time—to bring the Sun back to the same position in the observer's sky.

The same is true of the Moon, for, although it can make one

entire revolution about the Earth in a sidereal period of 27·321 days as measured against the starry background, the Earth, during the same period, has completed nearly one-twelfth of its orbit about the Sun at an average speed of some 18 miles per second.

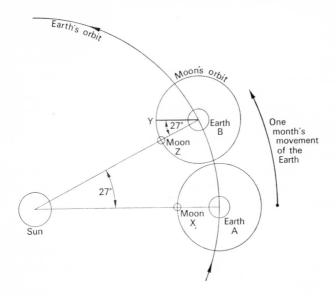

FIG. 7. The largest of the curved lines represents a part of the Earth's yearly orbit about the Sun. In a lunar "sidereal month" of 27·3 days the Earth moves from position A in its orbit to position B taking the Moon and its orbit with it. New Moon is indicated at X in the A diagram and the next "sideral" new Moon at Y in diagram B. But the Moon in the Y position does not line up with the Sun and Earth so the new Moon phase, as seen from Earth, cannot occur until the Moon has travelled the additional 27° angle in its orbit to bring it to point Z. Thus the synodical month of 29·5 days is 2·2 days longer than the sidereal month.

This fraction of the Earth's orbit is equivalent to an angle of nearly 27°, and, before the Moon can line itself up with the Sun again, it must overshoot by borrowing the required 27° from its next orbit. This means that from one new Moon to the next the Moon has to complete, instead of a normal sidereal revolution of 360°, a revolution amounting to 387°. The approximate numerical relationships between the synodical and sidereal months can be readily ascertained in the following way:

Duration of sidereal month: 27·3 days.

Angular value of lunar orbit completed in 1 day: $\dfrac{360}{27\cdot3} = 13\cdot2°$.

Time taken to complete an orbital revolution of 387°:

$$\frac{387}{13\cdot2} = 29\cdot4 \text{ days} \approx \text{synodical month.}$$

Actually the value of the synodical month is closer to 29·5 days, but the above calculation is close enough to show how the value is to be found. Besides, this is not a constant and its value varies by more than 13 hours, principally because of eccentricities in the lunar orbit (see also Fig. 7).

The remaining periods, the Tropical Month, the Anomalistic Month and the Nodical Month, are largely of academic interest to the astronomer. The first describes the motion of the Moon in relation to a point of the ecliptic called the equinox. The second is the month as measured from perigee to perigee when the Moon is closest to the Earth—this yields a value of 27·554 days. The last refers the lunar motion to a point on its orbit called the node. The tropical month has a value close to that of the sidereal month —27·321 days—the difference is to be found in the fourth and successive decimal places.

CHAPTER 3

Exploring the Lunar Surface

IN WINTER in the northern hemisphere the full Moon sweeps across
the sky at a good altitude and provides the terrestrial naked-eye
observer with excellent views of our closest celestial companion.
Anyone with normal eyesight will know that the Moon's disc
does not reflect the Sun's light uniformly: some areas are darker
than others, and there are also long light streaks that radiate from
brighter nuclei. Long before Galileo, in 1609, pointed his first
telescope at the sky, and by so doing unlocked the door to a
marvellous realm hidden beyond the wall of normal visual acuity,
the Moon was a world of myth and legend. Even today the "man
in the Moon", the "lady in the Moon", the "man with a bundle of
sticks" and numerous other characters and things can be seen by
naked-eye observers, and these same lunar markings have different
interpretations in various parts of the world; thus, the Japanese
associate "rabbits" with the Moon. This aspect alone would
provide the subject material for volumes much larger than this,
so let us take our leave of it, and discover the facts relating to these
mysterious markings.

The early telescopes were feeble and far from perfect instruments,
and it is not surprising that some of the astronomers who used
them made serious mistakes in interpreting what they saw. Having
had no other model but the Earth to guide them, and having
glimpsed lunar mountains and smooth areas, we cannot blame
them for believing that the Moon had its share of continents and
oceans too. As we shall see later on, the seventeenth-century
astronomers were sadly mistaken, but the picturesque names they
gave to those objects continue to be used, and to those who study

the Moon they are a link with an illustrious by-gone but never to be forgotten age.

Before we proceed, we ought to devise some approximate method of defining the position of a feature on the lunar disc, but prior to this, we must understand how the Moon appears when it is seen through an astronomical telescope. Unlike terrestrial telescopes and binoculars, the astronomical telescope employs the simplest optical system, which consists of an objective—a large lens of long focal length—and an eyepiece; and the observer, gazing through the instrument, sees everything inverted. By placing another eyepiece-type lens within the instrument it is possible to reinvert the images to make them right way up again. The obvious question to ask at this point is why don't the astronomers use this simple device? The answer is that there is no such thing as a perfect optical instrument, and the astronomer is far happier seeing sharply defined images upside-down if his only alternative is to observe inferior erect images, caused by the insertion of additional lenses, that also reduce the light-grasp of the telescope. There is no more hardship involved in observing an inverted image of the Moon than there is occasioned by motoring in another country where one has to drive on the opposite side of the road—it is merely a question of habit.

A system of selenographic coordinates has already been described briefly, and, useful as this is, it must be admitted that it takes even the astronomer some little time to familiarize himself with it. Because of this, the author is abandoning established coordinate systems in favour of one that is familiar to everyone. I am, of course, referring to the watch or clock face that may be superimposed invisibly upon the face of the Moon to permit us to establish our bearings with sufficient accuracy for the time being (see Fig. 8).

For our first telescopic view of the Moon it is better not to use a large telescope, for we wish to see the whole disc simultaneously, and the images formed in the principal focal plane of a large telescope are far too big to be accepted by ordinary eyepieces. A telescope with an objective 2 or 3 inches in diameter is just about right, for this will allow all of the lunar disc to be seen brightly enough without giving the observer temporary attacks of Moonblindness.

If we choose a night when the Moon is full we can observe the whole disc, and get acquainted with many lunar features that we can later observe through more powerful instruments.

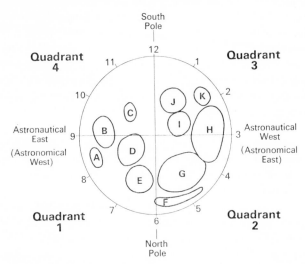

Fig. 8. This diagram represents the inverted disc of the Moon as seen through a small astronomical telescope. Clock-face numbers have been placed around the disc to assist with identification of lunar features. Approximate positions of maria are indicated. They are as follows: A, Crisium; B, Fecunditatis; C, Nectaris; D, Tranquillitatis; E, Serenitatis; F, Frigoris; G, Imbrium; H, Procellarum; I, Cognitum; J, Nubium; K, Humorum.

By common consent let us agree that our first telescopic view of the Moon reveals a truly inverted image of a circular disc in which the north pole appears at 6 o'clock at the bottom of the field of the eyepiece. The south pole is at 12 o'clock, while at 3 o'clock we have the *astronautical* west and at 9 o'clock the *astronautical* east. Astronautical easts and wests are similar to terrestrial easts and wests in the sense, that, if one faces to the north, the outstretched right hand points east, and the left hand west. As far as the Moon is concerned this convention is a modern development, adopted by the International Astronomical Union, for the convenience of lunar astronauts, who will have many other far more pressing problems to solve when they get on the Moon's surface. As might be expected, the *astronomical* eastern and western limbs are the opposite way round to their astronautical counterparts, and this is simply because these limbs are east or west of the centre of the lunar disc as we see it, without a telescope, in the sky. It is nevertheless the *astronomical* and *not* the astronautical values that are listed in the *Nautical Almanac* and other ephemerides.

If we are going to adopt a system of cardinal points, we might just as well choose the astronautical ones, since these are going to be more meaningful when the astronauts finally make their landings. So, recapitulating, the inverted lunar north, south, east and west are, respectively, 6, 12, 9 and 3 o'clock on our watch-face. So far so good; now let us draw a straight line between the north and south poles, and another between the most easterly and westerly points, thus cutting the lunar disc into four equal sections or *quadrants*. These are numbered 1, 2, 3 and 4 in the same manner and direction as the normal trigonometrical quadrants, except that our image is upside down, and lunar quadrant no. 1 comes in the quarter of the disc bounded by 9 and 6 o'clock; no. 2 comes between 6 and 3 o'clock, and so on. The numerical value of the quadrants increases in an anticlockwise direction no matter which way up the lunar disc is orientated.

Now we have sketched out a fairly substantial canvas upon which we can deploy our lunar features and details. The merest glance through our telescope will tell us that most of the brighter *"continental"* *areas* of the lunar crust are contained within quadrants 3 and 4 or, a little more precisely, between the hours of 10 and 1 on our clock-face. In the northern half of the disc, quadrant 1 takes the lion's share of what is left of the "continental" areas while there is some overspill into the limb regions of quadrant 2.

Thus, there is an arc of lunar continent that commences around 5 o'clock and finishes at 9.

As we would expect, the continental areas are those that contain the mountain masses as well as vast numbers of craters of all shapes and sizes. It is also fairly certain that these areas, in general, are higher in altitude than the darker *maria regions* of the Moon, and when we gaze at them through the telescope, the peace and tranquillity that we see is akin to that of a battlefield after a major engagement, for it is very evident that the convulsions that shaped the lunar crust were on a scale thousands of times greater than the world's most powerful nuclear bombs.

The lunar continents occupy about 60% of the visible lunar disc, so it does not require any Sherlock Holmes to deduce that the other 40% consists largely of what were once considered to be seas and oceans that are grouped under the Latin term *maria*. The most prominent of these is the Mare Imbrium (Sea of Showers) which takes up a large area of quadrant 2—the clock-hand at 5 o'clock bisects this enclosure. In all, there are eleven original maria, and most of them, like Mare Imbrium, are approximately circular in shape, being bounded by rougher and, in some cases, quite rugged mountainous country. Their names roll off the tongue like seventeenth-century poetry: Crisium (Crises), Fecunditatis (Fertility), Nectaris (Nectar or Honey), Tranquillitatis (Tranquillity), Serenitatis (Serenity), Vaporum (Mists), Nubium (Clouds), Humorum (Moisture) and Frigoris (Cold). As well as the maria, there is one ocean in the north-west (quadrant 2), the Oceanus Procellarum (Ocean of Storms) whose outlines are difficult to trace along its eastern boundary because it merges with Mare Imbrium.

When Ranger 7 crash-landed upon the lunar surface in the Guericke region, on 31st July, 1964, it was generally accepted that this area was a part of Mare Nubium. However, as there seemed to be some doubt about this fact, and just to clarify the position, the new name "Mare Cognitum" (Known Sea) was adopted by the International Astronomical Union at their meeting in Hamburg in August 1964. This brings the sum total of major seas and oceans up to 12, and examination of the chart in this book will show where they are to be found.

Having carved up the lunar surface into continents and seas, the reader might be pardoned for concluding that this constituted all that the early selenographers had achieved, but in this he would be merely indulging in self-delusion, for, at this stage, they had barely begun! Every major intrusion of the seas into the continen-

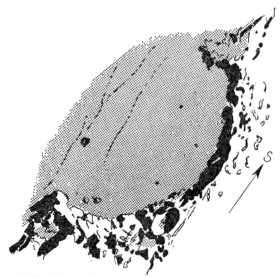

Fig. 9. The Sinus Iridum measures about 160 miles across and may be classified as an incomplete mare-type object.

tal masses were bays, and, as such they merited names. Thus we find, near the centre of the disc, the Sinus Aestuum (Seething Bay) and, on the northern edge of the Mare Imbrium, the Sinus Iridum (Bay of Rainbows) (see Fig. 9)—this is one of the few objects on the lunar crust that does have some association with its name, for the great regular arc of the Jura Mountains, that towers over the bay, is truly shaped like a rainbow. It was at the western end of this rainbow-arc that Cassini, another seventeenth-century map-maker, imagined that he saw mountains in the shape of a woman's head, and, accordingly, the face was inserted on his chart, and thus it can be seen today in the Royal Astronomical Society's Library in London. A few days before full Moon the solar illumination grazes across the surface of the Sinus Iridum, and the head of Cassini's lady can once more be seen by anyone possessing a modest telescope capable of magnifying a few dozen times.

Another bay that is conspicuous, by virtue of its position, is the Sinus Medii (Central Bay) and this is easy to find since the lines that define our four quadrants cross within it. This does not exhaust the list of bays, but we ought to pass on to other features possessing fanciful names including those that come under the headings of marshes and lakes. Among these we have the nightmarish Palus Putredinis (Marsh of Decay) within the eastern boundary of the Mare Imbrium, and the more restful Palus Somni (Sleep) on the eastern edge of the Mare Tranquillitatis. Among the lakes are the Lacus Somniorum (Lake of Dreams) and the Lacus Mortis (Death)—the latter is a grim name that may not inspire much optimism in the hearts of any astronautical crew that finds itself within its confines. These two lakes are to be found in the first quadrant north of the Mare Serenitatis—not so far from the 7 o'clock position on our clock-face.

As we strip off the veils of mystery that have shrouded the Moon for several millennia we begin to see how starkly barren and hostile our satellite really is. Even from the peaks of the long curvilinear mountain ranges, the views across the maria, in this land of near horizons, offer nothing but haunting vistas of harsh shadow and rocky wilderness. What is it, then, that beckons man on, and demands that he should risk life and limb to achieve the conquest of the Moon? It is true that national prestige has played a catalytic role that has probably advanced the sciences of astronautics by several decades, but this has done no more than underline the eternal truth that man, given reasonable, but by no means certain, odds is prepared to challenge the unattainable. Back in 1953, after the triumphant attempt on Mount Everest by Hillary and Tensing, Sir John Hunt, leader of the expedition, supplied the all-time answer to such questions: "... because it is there!"

Ringed Plains and Craters

It would have been satisfying for the author to have asserted that the phenomena that are typically "lunar" in origin and which may have no counterpart in the rest of the Solar System are the craters. The American space-craft Mariner, reaching the vicinity of Mars in 1965, soon dispelled this illusion. Mariner relayed back to the Earth pictures of Martian craters that could easily have been mistaken for lunar features, and, having digested this fragment of information, there seems to be no reason why the planet Mercury and a host of planetary satellites should not be festooned with similar formations.

The lunar craters occur in spectacular profusion, and in all sizes, in all parts of the lunar surface, although the incidence of craters is larger in the continental areas than in the maria. It is convenient to classify lunar craters into several categories, so, starting with the very large members of the crater family, we call these the "ringed plains". This is certainly a fair description, for their diameters are so vast and their ramparts, by comparison, so low, that, apart from being approximately circular, they bear little resemblance to true craters. The largest of these, on the hemisphere facing the Earth, is named Bailly, and its 180-mile span could engulf an area equal to half of that of England, or the combined total area of Belgium and the Netherlands, or, in the United States, an area of a State the size of West Virginia. Bailly is found at 1 o'clock in quadrant 3 of our chart. It is doubtful if there are larger "ringed plains" than Bailly on the whole Moon, and it is to be lamented that this huge enclosure is situated so close to the south-west lunar limbs that the libratory movements of the Moon often carry it into the averted hemisphere, and, even under the best observing conditions, it is still very foreshortened into what appears to be a narrow ellipse. Although we do not get good views of Bailly, there is another smaller, but, nevertheless, very fine example, of a ringed plain almost in the centre of the lunar disc. This one is called Ptolemaeus, after the great Ptolemy (A.D. 100–170) whose *Almagest* became a standard astronomical text for 1400 years. This feature is about half the diameter of Bailly—a mere 90 miles—but such is the curvature of the lunar surface that, if an observer were to stand in the smooth centre of

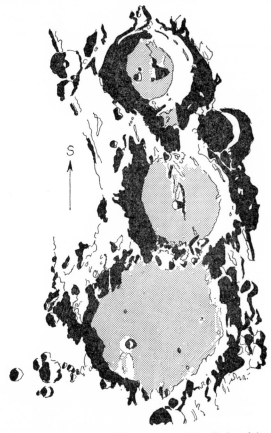

FIG. 10. Ptolemaeus (90 miles), Alphonsus (70 miles) and Arzachel (60 miles) are near the centre of the lunar disc in quadrant 3. No finer trio of large craters exists on the visible hemisphere.

Ptolemeus, the mountain walls, rising in some places to about 10,000 feet, would be almost completely hidden beyond the horizon (see Fig. 10).

Dimensionally, the ringed plains are selenological links between true craters and the maria, and, as such, they have diameters ranging upwards from about 50 miles to the already mentioned 180 miles of Bailly. In addition, there are two main types of ringed plain. The two that have already been mentioned are akin to small maria and, as such, do not have central peaks. Others, like the 140-mile Clavius in the lunar southern hemisphere, do have central peaks, and tend to resemble eroded over-sized craters, and the inner ramparts often fall gently to the floor of the ring in irregular systems of terraces. The shallower maria-like ringed plains have floors that are smoother and less broken by smaller craters, and, although the true mechanism remains to be discovered, it seems that these features may have started originally as large deep craters that were later filled with lava or magma flows. Thus any terraces on the primeval walls will be covered.

There are two other fine examples of small walled or ringed plains in the Mare Imbrium, that can be found on our chart in quadrant 2, or at approximately 6 o'clock on our lunar clock face. Archimedes is nearer to the middle of the disc than Plato, which does not occupy a place in the Mare so much as a position in the lunar Alps that overlook this vast plain. Of the two, Plato, with a span of 60 miles, is 10 miles larger in diameter than Archimedes. Again, these are mysterious objects that give every appearance of being deep craters that were inundated with the darker maria-type material during some earlier period in the Moon's history (see Fig. 11).

It is not the intention of the author to exhaust, by prolonged discussion, every detail on the lunar surface; besides if the reader wanted such information he would have had to invest in a small library of lunar books instead of this solitary volume. Instead we will visit the typical and the unusual, and as with most conducted tours the important items will be pointed out. When we visit a castle or a museum we seek out the architecture or *objets d'art* that interest us—we do not examine every stone with a magnifying glass or seek out individual brush-marks in the paintings.

Some of the earlier selenographers—Neison, for example, around the turn of the century—described crateriferous features under eight headings, but even the experts ran into difficulties with this system, and it now seems that the word "crater" has been tacitly adopted, more or less universally, to describe deep-walled features

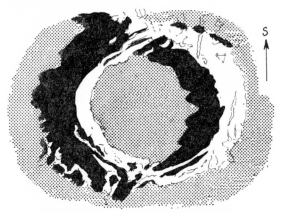

Fig. 11. Archimedes (50 miles diameter) as seen under late afternoon solar lighting conditions.

ranging in size from about 10 to 40 miles in diameter. There are a few exceeding 60 miles in diameter, such as Theophilus (see Fig. 12), which, to the author, seems to be more adequately described by the word "crater" than "ringed plain", for the latter name conjures up visions of shallow basins like the already mentioned Archimedes and Plato, whereas Theophilus, with a depth of nearly 3 miles, and possessing a group of central peaks that rise to about 4500 feet above the floor, is just as much a crater as Tycho or Copernicus. Theophilus is to be found on the western edge of Mare Nectaris, and is the most northerly of a chain of three large enclosures of which the other two are Cyrillus and Catharina. Cyrillus has the appearance of being an old and eroded crater, and it is particularly interesting to see that Theophilus, as well as appearing younger and more precipitous, has, by its own formation, forced aside the ramparts of Cyrillus. There are many examples of this phenomenon on the lunar surface, but, generally, the

FIG. 12. Theophilus (65 miles diameter) has by its more recent formation intruded into the perimeter of the slightly smaller Cyrillus. Catharina (top) completes a spectacular trio of large craters.

younger craters are smaller than those they have invaded—in this connection, Theophilus is an exception (see Fig. 13). However, the whole subject of crater formation is fascinating, and the estimation of their ages, which is partly aided by studying how some formations overlap others, is just one more link in a chain of knowledge that will some day tell us about the birth of the Moon four and a half thousand million years ago.

A few lines back we mentioned, for the first time, the craters Tycho and Copernicus, which are very well known because of the systems of bright rays that radiate from them, and which are particularly noticeable around full Moon. Any person possessing normal eyesight can see these light ray systems without optical aid, and a small telescope or binoculars will reveal them easily, as

FIG. 13. Stöfler, in quadrant 4, is a good example of a large lunar feature that has been partially obliterated by the younger and smaller formation, Faraday. Faraday, in turn, has two overlapping craters on its southern wall.

well as the central craters responsible for their formation. Before we go on to discuss some of the physical properties of these two craters, there are perhaps some readers who would like to know how they were given their names. To do this we must become travellers in time and return to A.D. 1650—the letters A.D. are very important—and find ourselves watching Riccioli of Bologna preparing a chart of the Moon for inclusion in his *Almagestum*

Novum. At this time there was still a great deal of division between astronomers as to whether the Sun or the Earth were the centre of the Solar System, and, since Riccioli favoured the latter view, that had also been vigorously held by the great Tycho Brahe (A.D. 1546–1601), who died less than one decade before the debut of Galileo's telescope, he allotted to Tycho the most conspicuous

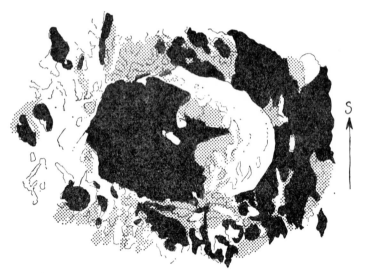

Fig. 14. Tycho (50 miles diameter), on account of its fine system of rays, is one of the most prominent craters on the Moon.

crater on the Moon. Other astronomers, Copernicus (A.D. 1473–1543), Kepler (A.D. 1571–1630) and Aristarchus of Samos (310–230 B.C.) who had rightly believed the Sun to be the centre of the Solar System, were assigned handsome craters set boat-like in a frozen Oceanus Procellarum that was, supposedly, alien to such mutinous notions.

We shall visit these three craters, for they are all interesting in different ways. First, however, let us examine the crater Tycho (see Fig. 14) which is a little more than 50 miles in diameter and has walls that rise above its floor to a height exceeding 16,000 feet. As is normal with this type of formation, there are terraces to be seen on the interior walls and these lead down to a floor that appears to be smooth when seen through a small telescope. A large one, however, reveals that it is far from smooth, for its 5000-foot central peaks are surrounded by hummocky terrain that could spell disaster for any astronautical vehicle that attempts to land inside this impressive circle. Despite this, the floor of Tycho is smoother than the immediate environs. This is a region of ringed plains and craters of all shapes and sizes, and obviously one where any increase of optical resolution will show smaller and smaller craterlets. If this had been one of the Ranger areas it is certain that the vehicle's sharp-eyed cameras would have recorded thousands of tiny craterlets just before the moment of impact.

The Tycho ray system (see Plate 1) is the largest on the visible hemisphere of the Moon, and it is characterized by the form of individual rays which can be traced to distances of about 1000 miles away from the parent crater. The crater itself is surrounded by a diffused ring of darker material of no appreciable thickness, which is about 100 miles in diameter. It is from this that the rays seem to radiate, and it is possible that this area—to borrow from the radio hams' vocabulary—formed a kind of skip distance beyond which fell most of the material ejected from the crater. Although it is by no means certain as to what caused such a cataclysmic disturbance, there can be little doubt that the rays we see from the Earth are composed of vast numbers of overlapping plumes of debris that were displaced by the secondary impacts of large and small boulders. Taking as an example just one plume of dust and one boulder there is no difficulty in understanding the ray-forming mechanism: the boulder describes its low-level trajectory from the parent crater and strikes the ground where it displaces a splash of debris and dust that, although fanned out comet-like from the point of impact, still continues to point arrow-like back in the direction of the parent crater. From our scrutiny of the Tycho ray system we can see, since the rays are long and narrow and tend to point directly at the crater, that the fragments that caused the secondary impacts were ejected like sticks of bombs to fall along great circles that passed through Tycho. However, the impact points of ejected boulders need not line up symmetrically with the parent crater, although in general the secondary "raylets" will, so, where a ray does not seem to radiate from the central crater, we have an initial deployment of ejected boulders that land at varying distances from the epicentre. If a straight line were drawn to connect the separate points of impact, it is more than likely that the same line would not pass through the parent crater. There are several instances of this, and the ray that falls south of Tycho towards the limb is a good example, and it is again worth stressing the point that the individual raylets still point back at Tycho even if the main ray does not. In this way the raylets may be likened to rusted weather-vanes that continue to point in the direction from whence came the last hurricane-force wind that was able to turn them.

Perhaps the question asked most often about the craters is "what caused them?" and from a number of theories we can select two that still enjoy a popularity that, like the phases of the Moon, have waxed and waned for more than a century. Both are reasonable in the sense that we can produce terrestrial examples of either type of crater, so it would not demand a great deal of imagination to hazard at least the guess that one of the mechanisms was volcanic in origin. The other theory describes how craters can be formed by the impacts of large meteorites, and, again, we can point to a few terrestrial examples, the most celebrated being the Arizona meteor crater within a few miles of the famous Lowell Observatory in the U.S.A. The main weakness with both these explanations is that of size: on the Moon we have enormous craters, like Theophilus and Tycho, which are ten times the diameter of the largest volcanic craters on the Earth, and as regards the comparison of meteoric craters the ratio goes up still more to about 50:1. For example, a quite powerful telescope is required to show a lunar crater as small as the Arizona crater, which is four-fifths of a mile across. The number of Arizona-type craters on the Moon runs into hundreds of thousands.

Already, it seems, we are submerged in difficulties, but, fortunately, there is an escape-hatch which may help. The Moon, for reasons that we shall discuss later, can be regarded as a celestial museum piece or, to make matters clearer, astronomers can think of no mechanism that can exercise sufficient energy on the surface to obliterate quickly the primeval lunar features. This, in fact, and according to another theory, can take us back to a remote time when the lunar crust was in a semi-molten state. On the Earth the situation is entirely different: around the coasts of the British Isles the sea claims considerable volumes of precious land each year. In addition, the rains wash soil into the rivers and the rivers transport it down to the sea. The Earth is a place of change, mountains rise out of the sea to be planed down again by ice, snow, wind and rain—the process never stops. On the geological scale vast transformations have taken place on the Earth within a few thousands of years. Not so the Moon. The face of the Moon, that gazed blindly down when the "lords of the Earth" were giant reptiles and dinosaurs, looked almost the same then as it does today—the passage of several million years may have added a few new scars, but the main lunar features remain largely unchanged. When we observe this Sphinx-like world, we see in its mountains, plains, craters and rays a record of all the forces that have combined to mould the surface as we now see it. Eventually these cosmic hieroglyphics will yield their secrets, but not until the astronomers find the key in some as yet undiscovered celestial Rosetta Stone. It is evident that no one theory accounts for all of the diversities of this alien world: some sort of vulcanism can hardly have failed to have played a part, and many of the smaller craters are undoubtedly the result of meteoric impact. If the Earth were ever pock-marked with craters as large as Theophilus this would have been so long ago that all traces of them would have been effaced by the elements, and in passing we ought not to forget that a burst of energy sufficient to excavate a lunar Theophilus would not produce a crater of this size on the Earth: however, this is another story that must wait its turn.

Quadrant 2, between 3 and 6 o'clock on our clock-face, contains more maria surface than any other quadrant on the visible hemi-sphere, and it is in these regions of the Mare Imbrium and Oceanus Procellarum that we find the craters Copernicus, Kepler and Aristarchus—you will recall Riccioli's reason for naming these craters in this way. Apart from the near-by Eratosthenes,

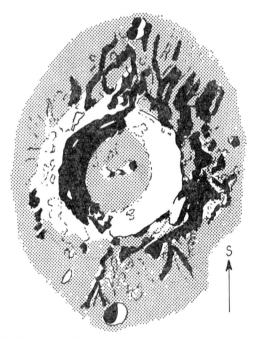

Fig. 15. Copernicus (57 miles diameter) possesses a system of rays that is second only to that of Tycho.

and discounting the ringed plains of Archimedes and Plato, Copernicus (see Fig. 15) is the only large crater in quadrant 2, and it is made even more conspicuous by its central position and grand ray system. In size, Copernicus comes between Theophilus and Tycho and has a diameter of about 57 miles. None of these craters are perfectly circular: in fact their shapes are more aptly described as irregular polygons, and, in the case of Copernicus, one can trace, without too much difficulty, long stretches of nearly straight exterior ramparts. Ignoring smaller undulations of the walls, the form of Copernicus approximates to that of a hexagon (six-sided). Thus the error in measuring the diameter of such a feature may amount to a few per cent, depending from which points the measurements are actually made.

Inside Copernicus, the walls tumble down abruptly at first, and then in a cascade of irregular terraces to a 40-mile-diameter floor that is almost circular in shape, and which surrounds a small and inconspicuous group of three separated central peaks. These are much smaller than those that grace the interiors of Theophilus and Tycho, and it is doubtful if any future astronaut would bother to climb them, for, having scaled the highest of them, his vantage-point would still be less than one-quarter of the height of the 12,000-foot surrounding walls, but from the tops of the walls he would command a magnificent view of the whole crater. The floor of Copernicus is smoother to the north, while, south of the central peaks, we again get the impression of hummocky ground similar to the floor of Tycho.

The outer ramparts of Copernicus, as one might expect, are less steep than the slopes of the interior, and their height above the general level of the surrounding mare is about 3000 feet, which means that the floor of the crater is 9000 feet lower than the local environs.

The Copernican rays system is more compact than that of Tycho. None of the individual rays can be traced farther than about 500 miles from the site of the primary explosion. There are other differences too: Copernicus is not encircled by a ring of diffused darker material, although there is some evidence of local darkenings to the north-west of the crater. More interesting, however, are two small dark circular areas that intrude into the ray system south of the crater; there is another to the north, and these three contain craterlets, and it would be reasonable to deduce that these came into existence after the formation of the rays, for, if it were not so, how can we explain why they were not covered by the dust and debris that came out of the parent crater? It is by such methods that selenologists determine an approximate time-scale that reveals, if not the actual age, at least the sequence of lunar events.

In this type of study, it is necessary to observe the full Moon, or to examine the best available full Moon photographs, for the deployment of the ray systems cannot be analysed properly if some of the lunar surface is hidden in shadow—this is why the rays are not very prominent when seen under low Sun angles. If the small dark areas are more recent than the Copernican rays, there is also some evidence to support the view that Copernicus postdates the 38-mile-diameter crater Eratothenes which occupies a mare position some 180 miles to the north-east of Copernicus. Under full Moon illumination, Eratosthenes clearly shows a dusting of ray material on the outer and inner ramparts facing Copernicus, while the averted slopes display shadings where the low trajectory ray debris did not fall: there is also a ray "shadow" crossing the floor, evidently caused by the shielding action of the central peaks. Such is the message of the lunar rocks in the vicinity of Eratosthenes.

South of Eratosthenes, the telescope reveals large Copernican ray areas that, at first sight, display little or no alignment at all. Closer study reveals, however, that this disorderly mass of dust and debris is not so randomly distributed as it appears to be at first sight. Immediately south and extending well to the east of Eratosthenes is a delicate elliptical ray showing a very defined edge against darker mare material. To the south-east of Copernicus a nearly circular ray of light material, with a smaller but similar ray asymmetrically placed within it to the north, has splashed over the darker maria surface. There are no finer arched or looped rays than this on the visible hemisphere. Apart from these exceptions, the Copernican rays are not so clearly defined as those of Tycho, but a long one, that falls to the north across the Mare Imbrium, after emerging from the tangled interweave of local rays, is an impressive example of the type of ray that does not seem to originate in the parent crater.

PLATE 1.
Photographed with the 24-inch refracting telescope at the Pic-du-
Midi Observatory on 22nd October, 1964 at 01 hours 54 minutes
02 seconds U.T. (G.M.T.) this picture shows the Moon just after
the full phase. Note the extensive ray systems of Tycho, Copernicus
and Kepler; the brilliant Aristarchus and the darker maria.

West of Copernicus there is an area in which the Copernican rays are seen to cross those of Kepler, and, in essence, if we could establish which ones were uppermost we could then state which crater was the older. Perhaps this is a problem that will yield to new methods: for example, if the colours of the two ray systems are slightly different there is a possibility of being able to emphasize these colour differences by special photometric techniques.

Our selenological tour has shown us three mighty craters of roughly similar dimensions, and there can be little doubt that similar forces brought them into being. Nevertheless, each is a variation on a theme, and, before leaving them, we ought to mention some of the points in which they differ. Some space has been devoted to the ray systems of Tycho and Copernicus, and the reader may have wondered why, so far, there is no description of a Theophilus ray system. Now most scientists, I think, will agree with a certain unwritten premise which might have stated that "if it exists, it can be described". "It", in the present context, represents the Theophilus ray system, and, at first sight, it is difficult to trace it at all, for Theophilus occupies a position on the lunar disc where two other ray systems cross. Some of the great splashes of bright dust originate in Tycho, while others come from the Stevinus area in quadrant 4—round about 10 o'clock on our clock face. To complicate further the search for these elusive remnants, the southern and north-eastern and north-western local surroundings of the crater are light and are further embellished with small bright craters, many of them possessing miniature ray systems of their own. It is evident that our quest in these areas is doomed to failure before it even starts, and, having subtracted these regions, we are left with two dark maria areas, Nectaris, to the east, and Tranquillitatis, to the north. Mare Nectaris is crossed by a number of rays from Stevinus and Tycho, and there is a particularly fine example of a crater—evidently a secondary crater from Tycho—with a plume of dust pointing back along the great circle route to this great ring. Our search in southern Mare Tranquillitatis is more rewarding: there are five vestiges of faded rays, and three of these fan out to form a broad overall misty

M.I.F.—C

elliptical ray which has sometimes been mistaken for a thumb print on our lunar negatives. This resembles, except for its faintness, the broad elliptical Copernican ray that we have noted already.

Having at last detected the remains of a Theophilus ray system, the next question to ask is, "Why is it so inconspicuous?" This is a problem that interests the physicists very much; and laboratory experiments have been conducted by Gold and others, and their results indicate that lunar rays simply fade away under the continual bombardment of radiation from the Sun. During these investigations it was discovered that certain powdered terrestrial rocks darken by simulated solar radiation so, since the case seems to be proven, we have another possible method by which we can measure the comparative ages of lunar features, and not only the rays, for crater material fades as well. If we re-examine this trio of giant craters, under full Moon illumination, we can see that each possesses a bright rim of what might well be ray material: it is just as if someone wished to delineate the crater perimeters by painting a bright line round the upper, and inner, ramparts of each crater. Tycho has a fine bright rim which is further emphasized by the darker diffused circle outside the crater. Copernicus also has such a rim but it is not so perfect as that of Tycho, but despite this the whole Copernican crater is brighter than either Tycho or Theophilus. In the competition for refulgence, Theophilus comes a poor third, and from this we may conclude that this crater is older than the two brighter ones, and, as a consequence of its age, it has become "tarnished" and the brighter inner ramparts and central peaks are the only reminders of its former glory.

Soon we must continue our lunar tour, but, before we leave the subject of fading craters and ray systems, it is only fair to the reader to point out, that, while it is wholly tenable that such phenomena take place, the mere fact that scientists can produce the same effect in the laboratory does not constitute proof. Millions of years are involved, and there may be other agencies at work, and one, at least, readily springs to mind—micrometeorites. We are sometimes painfully aware of the effects of hailstones if we are caught out in a shower. Micrometeorites can also occur in showers, and unlike hailstones that possess velocities of a few dozen feet per second, we are here dealing with much smaller bodies with velocities of 10 to 20 *miles* per second! At the present time satellite-borne instruments tell us that the volume of cosmic space that surrounds the Earth is sparsely populated with such bodies. What we would like to know is the flux density of the small particles of matter that showered into the Earth–Moon system millions of years ago, when conditions were very different. Forces such as these, depending on velocities, sizes and frequency of the impacting bodies, as well as the durations of the showers which themselves may have persisted sporadically for hundreds, thousands or even millions of years, would have transformed by erosion the appearance of any celestial body that lacked the protection of an atmosphere.

There are far too many answer-starved cosmic questions. In the case of the faded crater Theophilus and its phantom ray system, there is yet another possible explanation: perhaps this crater never had an extensive ray system at all. Remembering that, of the three, Theophilus is the largest, and that the bigger the crater the larger are the forces required to excavate it, and also bearing in mind the very extensive ray system of Tycho with thousand-mile-long rays, we might ask ourselves what would have happened if the forces responsible for Tycho had been much larger. In this context we must also memorize the lunar escape velocity which is about one-fifth of the Earth's or rather less than 1·5 miles per second, for if a solid body, such as a stone or boulder, attains this velocity, by whatever means, it will escape from the Moon and be lost in space. In the case of Tycho, the smallest of the trio, one might attempt to explain its far-flung ray system by making the assumption that most of the ejecta just failed to escape because the energy of the initial explosion was insufficient. Copernicus, which is somewhat larger than Tycho, may have yielded enough energy to launch a sizeable percentage of its erstwhile contents into space, and this might explain the smaller ray system surrounding a larger crater. Using the same argument again, would it be unreasonable to ask if the parallel process, in the case of Theophilus, resulted in the almost total loss into space of most of its ejected fragments?

No final answers to these questions are forthcoming as yet, and the mechanisms that we have been reviewing may be connected with lunar matters, or, again, they may not, for we have reached an epoch where long-established lunar theories may, like the rays, fade away under the bright light of newly acquired knowledge.

Four hundred miles due west of Copernicus is the bright crater Kepler, which is 22 miles in diameter and has walls that rise about 10,000 feet above its floor. Kepler, on its own, is not a remarkable formation, its floor is far from smooth, and dimensionally there are many other lunar craters that are superior to it, and were it not for its location in the Oceanus Procellarum, where it occupies, almost spiderlike, the centre of a fine system of rays, it is more than likely that the observer's eye would pass on to some other more rewarding feature. Earlier, we noted that certain components of the ray systems of Copernicus and Kepler actually cross each other, and the same is true of the rays coming from the 29-mile-diameter Aristarchus which lies about 400 miles north-west of Kepler. In fact an isosceles triangle of rays unites the three craters, but those emanating from Aristarchus are less bright than those of Kepler and Copernicus. Not to be outdone, however, Aristarchus restores the balance by being the brightest crater on the visible hemisphere of the Moon, and its central peak is the most brilliant spot on the visible lunar hemisphere.

The whole area of these craters is full of interest: for example, to the north-west of Aristarchus we have one of the oddest formations on the Moon; this is the Schröter's Valley (see Fig. 16) that resembles a dried-up river-bed. Starting from a crater-like hollow west of Aristarchus, and north of the smooth-floored Herodotus, the valley proceeds in a northerly direction for about 20 miles before veering off sharply to the north-west at an angle of about 120°. After making this turn, the course of the valley is reasonably straight for about 10 miles, then it begins to zigzag, turning abruptly north to form the first stroke of a compact letter W—

this is a part of the valley where small craterlets are visible in a powerful telescope. And, as if not quite certain as to what to do next, the valley, after completing the W, turns to the north-west once more for about 5 miles, then, veering again by a right angle to the south-west, it proceeds in this direction, not without some

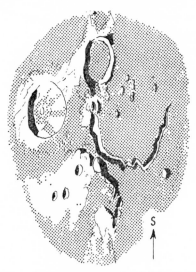

FIG. 16. Aristarchus (29 miles) is the brightest crater on the visible hemisphere of the Moon. Schröter's Valley (Vallis Schröteri) often gives the mistaken appearance of a forked valley with one component progressing north. The true valley has an irregular U-shape as shown.

sinuousity, for about 40 miles until it is lost in the Oceanus Procellarum. Schröter's Valley is best observed about 1 day before the full Moon when a modest telescope will show it without difficulty.

The 64,000-dollar question concerning this and other valleys or *rilles* on the lunar surface is: "What agency caused them?" Were they ever water-courses, or, if not for water, were they channels for some other liquid? Most investigators dismiss these ideas, for as long as we assume that the physical conditions on the Moon have remained unchanged for most of its history, we have to accept also the rapid boiling off into space of any lunar water that found its way to the surface.

These are topics that merit more space later on, and we will return to them.

Bounded on the south-east by Schröter's Valley and stretching away to the north-west—we are still in quadrant 2, at about 4 o'clock—is a large area, an ill-defined parallelogram of lunar surface, of about 10,000 square miles area. This is called Wood's Spot, after a celebrated scientist, R. W. Wood, who in 1910 published papers relating to photographic work performed in the ultra-violet and the red that had revealed that this area possesses a definite colour. Until that time, the idea of colours on the Moon had gained little ground, or, if you like, the lunar ground had gained little colour, and, even today these delicate hues are very difficult to observe visually, and, to do this success-fully, the observer must have access to a large telescope and must keep his images small and bright, being careful to avoid the type of eyepiece that gives a large magnification accompanied by a dilution of the light and a loss of colour contrast.

By such means, the author observed the colour of Wood's Spot with the 43-inch reflector at the Pic-du-Midi Observatory in the French Pyrenees, and it is best described as a straw colour. Digressing, momentarily, it can be said that most astronomical colours are "delicate"—this applies to stars and planets—and, if these colours have to be observed visually, a large telescope is required. Photographic observations can be accomplished with smaller instruments, for example, the author has taken ultra-violet and red photographs of Wood's Spot with a 6-inch reflecting telescope, and the ultra-violet photograph shows it clearly, while, in the red, there is little to be seen of it. The explanation is, that, since the spot is yellowish, it cannot reflect violet light, and there-fore it appears dark on the ultra-violet photograph. Through the red filter the yellow area is reflecting approximately the same amount of light as the area surrounding Wood's Spot, and this time the photographic plate finds it difficult to separate one area from the other. There are other coloured areas on the lunar surface, but this one is the most prominent and therefore the best known, and since the colour is yellowish, there are some investigators who subscribe to the belief that this part of the Moon is covered with sulphur. There is a very real connection between sulphur and vulcanism, and we must add the name of this area to those that are already listed for the attention of visiting astronauts before this problem can be solved.

Obviously we could remain in this part of quadrant 2 for a considerable time, and we would, if the sole purpose of this little volume were to provide a dissertation on lunar surface features alone.

Moving eastwards away from Aristarchus, and skirting north of the horse-shoe of Prinz—evidently this was once a large ring that has become half submerged in Procellarian material—we pass a group of six small serpentine valleys that are reminiscent of Schröter's Valley (see Fig. 17), and which in three instances either start or finish—it is difficult to say which—in saucer-like depressions. These are mysterious objects that, to the author, always evoke impressions of ancient water-courses. In these cases the "streams" poured into the saucer-like depressions thus forming "lakes". The author hastens to add that these terms are being used descriptively: the true picture is very different and, again, these features are probably outward and visible signs of extinct lunar vulcanism. These, apart from being fine examples of valleys or rilles that terminate in rimless depressions, are typical of clefts and rilles that can be found in all parts of the lunar disc.

Let us now move swiftly across the Mare Imbrium and aim for an area about half-way between Plato, to the north, and Archimedes to the south. In crossing the mare we are traversing one of the most featureless areas of the Moon, but even here, where large craters are few and far between, these areas are still fairly well populated with small craters of around the same dimensions as the terrestrial one in Arizona. These bald lunar plains are so devoid of vertical relief that it is here that we can, at last, appreciate the nearness of lunar horizons, and we can sympathize with astronauts who get separated from the main party. It is certain that the first astronauts to visit the Moon will not be set tasks that will involve them in journeys away from the landing area. Later, when local

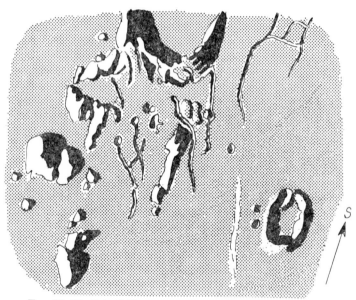

FIG. 17. The Prinz Rilles are a few miles east of the brilliant crater, Aristarchus. Part of the northern wall of Prinz is shown at the top of the figure.

explorations are authorized, those involved will have good reason to remember that the curvature of the lunar surface over the modest distance of 3 miles is sufficient to hide one 6-foot-high astronaut from another. The American Apollo Project that has as its aim the task of placing two men on the Moon, involves the use of a lunar module which will be 19 feet high as it stands on the lunar plains. This, too, will sink beyond the horizon of any member of the crew who wanders more than $4\frac{1}{2}$ miles away from it.

Taking a few more examples, our 6-foot-high astronaut would be out of sight of a 100-foot-high space-ship at a distance of $7\frac{1}{2}$ miles, while, at 20 miles, an object as high as the Eiffel Tower (900 feet) would be below his horizon. An edifice or hill matching in height the altitude of New York's Empire State Building (1500 feet) would likewise disappear at 25 miles.

By way of comparison we could conduct similar experiments to assess the effects of curvature of the Earth's surface as long as it were possible to find a suitable terrestrial location. Perhaps a long strip of frozen lake or river surface would meet the requirement whence it could be established that two 6-foot-high skaters, separated by a distance of 6 miles, would be unaware of each other's presence because each would be below the other's horizon.

There is a simple rule that we can use on the Earth to determine the distance of the horizon from any elevated vantage-point. If we compute the square root of the vertical height given in feet, and express the result in nautical miles (1 nautical mile = 6000 feet), this provides us with the approximate distance of the horizon. For example, if an observer is looking out to sea from the top of a 100-foot-high cliff this rule will enable him to calculate that his horizon is 10 nautical miles distant. The true value is $10 \cdot 63$ nautical miles.

By using similar methods we can ascertain that the terrestrial horizons of the Eiffel Tower and the Empire State Building ought to be, respectively, 37 and 47 statute miles (5280 feet) distant from their respective centres of origin. If these distances seem excessive, let us remember that neither of these edifices is located ideally to facilitate this type of observation, for Paris and, to a lesser degree, New York are surrounded by low hills; and in addition, we have also to contend with mist, smoke and dust in the Earth's atmosphere.

The nearness of the lunar horizons, coupled with unfamiliar and barren landscapes liberally bespattered with small circular craters of up to a few hundred yards across, pose bewildering problems for the astronaut who may have to pioneer his way across this celestial desert. The Russian Lunik 10 which went into orbit around the Moon on 3rd April, 1966 has detected a weak magnetic field, but insufficient information is available at the time of writing to know if this field is powerful enough to attract a compass needle. It seems likely that, instead of the compass needle by which terrestrial travellers find their way, the lunar counterpart will be a complicated box of electronics miniaturized to about the same dimensions. Despite this possibility, a refresher course in stellar navigation would be a useful way of occupying some of the time of the astronauts during the weeks of preparation for the final countdown, for, like the mariners of old, they would be able to fix their positions by the stars. With no clouds to cover the black lunar skies, it will be a simple matter to read off the sextant positions of the stars, and this information will be transmitted back to electronic computers on the Earth, and in a few seconds the true position of the expedition will be known by its members. The task of charting the Moon is well under way, and the best charts at the present time, on a scale of 16 miles to the inch, are being made by the U.S. Air Force at St. Louis, U.S.A.

Continuing eastward across the Mare Imbrium, we at last approach a feature, that, at a distance of 50 miles, just commences to loom on our horizon. As we approach this isolated mountain, we get the impression of a gigantic iceberg floating in a frozen sea, for there is little local relief around it, and this 7500-feet massif rises abruptly out of the plain. Piton (see Fig. 18) is one of several isolated peaks in this part of the Mare Imbrium, but there is nothing very dramatic about its outline despite the spire-like shadows that fall away from it under low Sun angles. From north to south its total length is 18 miles, and its east–west span is about the same.

Pico, a few miles south of the great walled-plain Plato, is almost a twin to Piton. This peak rises serenely above the plain to a height of 8000 feet, and, from its summit, the southern ramparts of Plato would dominate its northern horizon.

There are three other main groups of objects that preserve the characteristics of isolated peaks in the eastern Mare Imbrium. To the north-west of Pico, making a lop-sided V with the southern limb pointing at Pico, are the Teneriffe Mountains consisting of four main masses separated by the gently curving surface of the Mare. The highest points of this system do not exceed 8000 feet. To the west again there is the appropriately named Straight Range

S

Fig. 18. The isolated mountain, Piton, in the eastern Mare Imbrium, as it appeared to the author using the 24-inch refractor at the Pic-du-Midi Observatory on 23rd July, 1962. These isolated mountains appear to be more dramatic than they are due to the angles of solar illumination. Piton, from the lunar surface, is no more spectacular in shape than an upturned saucer.

which occupies an unnamed Imbrian bay between Plato and the Sinus Iridum. The most cursory glance with a modest telescope shows the straightness of this 40-mile-long range, but a powerful instrument is required to explore its pummelled and broken heights that attain a modest 6000 feet. Far to the south, a few miles north of Archimedes, are the Spitzbergen Mountains, a triangular group composed of six main units which, presumably, to those who named them, resemble the Spitzbergen Islands in the

Arctic Ocean. This resemblance is not very marked, but one may search the Earth maps in vain for groups of islands that would have been better terrestrial similitudes. The highest Spitzbergen peaks rise to little more than 5000 feet.

This, then, is a brief résumé of the main features of these strangely isolated mountains, and one may well ask how typically continental massifs such as these came to be situated in the maria regions. To the east of Piton, the lunar Alps cease abruptly as if to make way for the crater Cassini to the south-east, but between them there is more than enough undisturbed surface to contain Piton itself, and, since the latter is so obviously Alpine in character, one wonders if, at some remote time in the past, Piton were ever joined to the lunar Alps. Such lines of thought lead us into other mental cul-de-sacs that are without obvious exits. If we postulate a theory such as this, we have also to invoke enough energy to push or float—depending on the mechanism involved—the vast mass of Piton some 60 miles across the surface of the Mare to its present site. If we do not, we have to assume that these mountains were in their present positions all the time, and this may provoke other difficult questions, for it seems unreasonable to suppose that they were formed as isolated masses, and, if they were not, what has happened to the ranges to which they belonged originally? Closer examination of the areas in which these mountains stand reveals that most of them are associated with low and often wide maria ridges that, due to their serpentine appearances, are sometimes called "wrinkle ridges". These typically lunar features are seldom more than 1000 feet in height—most of them are considerably less—but their widths vary from a few to several miles—it is difficult to be more specific than this—and their lengths are frequently of such dimensions that, under low Sun angles, one may trace their outlines across several hundreds of miles of maria surface. For example, there is a very fine wrinkle ridge that crosses the Mare Serenitatis from north to south, at which extremity it almost merges with an extension of the Haemus Mountains which was named—perhaps with excessive grandiosity—Promontorium Archerusia! In the Mare Crisium, at 8 o'clock on our watch-face, another low serpentine ridge traverses the eastern side of the Mare and terminates to the south, near a promontory called Promontorium Agarum. Returning to the region of Cassini's Moon Maiden at the western end of the Sinus Iridum—this is at 5 o'clock —the promontory that forms the "head of the Maiden" is called Heraclides, after a philosopher who lived at Pontus about 300 B.C., and it is possible, particularly under low Sun angles, to trace a low ridge, or rather a whole system of parallel ridges, from here, across what appears to be a typical mare-like surface, to the Promontorium Laplace at the other end of the Jura Mountain range. At some earlier epoch in the Moon's history there may have been a complete Sinus Iridum enclosure: if so, these ridges may be remnants of former mountain walls that have been demolished by some mysterious process. To travel along the crests of these ridges from Promontorium Heraclides to Promontorium Laplace involves a physical journey of about 150 miles that, in a sense, is symbolic of a voyage in time from the forgotten works of Heraclides to those of the great French astronomer and mathematician, Pierre Simon Laplace (1749–1827). He scarcely needs a lunar monument to preserve his memory for, 50 years after his death, the French Academy of Science published his complete works in thirteen thick volumes!

In these three instances—and these are by no means unique on the lunar surface—we have continental mountain ranges that may be associated with the ridges that cross the maria areas. Sometimes such ridges form almost circular enclosures and, being ever mindful of all the other more prominent circular enclosures on the lunar surface, it would not be unreasonable to suppose that these, at any rate, are submerged craters that were filled and surrounded and, maybe, even partially melted by the substance that invaded them. As we shall see later, there were until recently two main streams of opinion; one supporting the concept of the maria areas being vast seas of once-molten lava. The other postulated enormous lunar dust-bowls, but this theory now has to be abandoned in view of the discoveries of Lunik 9 to which we shall return.

"The return of one swallow does not make a summer" is a true enough adage that has sufficient flexibility to be applied to the Moon, for it is probably equally true to argue, since the Lunik 9 took pictures of only one very restricted area of the lunar surface, that the surface that was examined and found to be devoid of dust is not typical of the Moon. The author feels that this surface is typical of the maria regions except where they are crossed by the great ray systems—here one would expect to find ejecta containing large quantities of pulverized rock and dust. This, however, is a private opinion; nevertheless if the Lunik 9 photographs are accepted as showing typical lunar surface, and the indications show this tendency, then the weather-vane of opinion must eventually orient itself in the direction of magma and lava flows, because these are the only major alternatives. This also implies some reorientation of the theories pertaining to the early history of the Moon, for if the maria areas have been molten at some stage this means that the Moon has gone through a hot stage and is cooling or has cooled off completely. With the dust theories the Moon could have started as a cool body (see also pp. 81, 82).

If the magma or lava theory is true we could expect certain conditions to arise within the body of the Moon that would result in the elevation of temperatures to around 1000–1500°C in the subsurface rocks. This would be sufficient to melt them partially or at least to make them viscous; at the same time it seems improbable that the outer crustal rocks would have become heated enough to cause their actual melting—one reason would be the very rapid dissipation of heat into surrounding space. We can therefore imagine a situation where large areas of the crust would become partially molten, while others, due to inhomogeneities in the thickness and thermal properties of the crustal materials, might escape this drastic phase. We would also have to suppose that the crustal plastic phase was a brief one, for, having broken through the insulating surface of the Moon, the heat would radiate very quickly into space, and the surface would once again become solid, but we might also expect to see remnants of former mountain ranges and craters. The true nature of the mechanism is still very mysterious, but if this outline were approximately true, the surrounding walls of ringed plains like Archimedes and Plato, during the plastic phase, would be little more than circular rocky ramparts that had escaped melting because of their low thermal conductivity. They would have something in common with an old leaky boat resting on a shallow river-bed; the water inside rapidly fills up to the level of the river, and only a few upper timbers rise to maintain the outline of the boat. In the case of the much larger Sinus Iridum, events evidently took a more dramatic turn, and the whole southern wall, between the two promontoria, partially melted and solidified into the wrinkle ridges we observe today. Following a similar line of reasoning, Pico, Piton and the other isolated mountains on the Mare Imbrium may well be the fragments of large mountain ranges that once dominated the youthful surface of the Moon.

Between Archimedes and the Imbrium/Serenitatis Straits, farther east, are the magnificent craters Autolycus and Aristillus (see Plate 1), both of which possess extensive ray systems, although these are by no means as fine as those of Tycho or Copernicus. Autolycus is the smaller of the two with a diameter of about 25 miles, while Aristillus measures 35 miles, and, in examining them through the telescope, this difference of size leads one to suspect that Aristillus is the deeper of the two. In fact, this is true, but the difference is not profound, for a recent height analysis made by the author reveals that the western walls of Autolycus rise to an average height of 10,300 feet above the floor, while the western, and, incidentally, the higher walls of Aristillus ascend to 10,700 feet. Neither crater has the smooth-floor characteristics of the shallower Archimedes, and the centre of Aristillus is dominated by a compact trio of peaks, the highest of which rises 3000 feet above the floor. There can be no doubt that these craters are comparatively late arrivals, for had they been excavated simultaneously with Archimedes, their floors also would have been flooded with maria material. Other indisputable evidence is revealed by studying the ray system of Autolycus: here we observe that two rays actually cross Archimedes, and this can only be explained on the assumption that the Archimedean floor had become solid before the arrival of the ejecta from Autolycus. Even this is not all: Aristillus is a classical crater in its own right by virtue of a fine system of radial ridges that descend from the outer ramparts on to the surrounding plain, and in so doing, they partially obliterate a *ghost crater* (see Fig. 19) situated a few miles from the northern rim of Aristillus. Let us assume, by way of explanation, that the forces that moulded the ringed plain Archimedes into its present form did not cease, but continued to erode or melt the walls until only the highest points were left above the surface of the mare. Then solidification took place, leaving a maria surface with a thin circular ridge of slightly elevated material to indicate the position of the entombed late-lamented ghost crater. To have a ghost crater so close to Aristillus rids us of an objection that might have cast doubt on the plausibility of Archimedean mechanisms being active in the Aristillus region. In other words, we have direct evidence of indications of ancient craters in this area, and, indeed, as far again to the north-east, where Cassini, a crater about the size of Aristillus, shows us what the latter might have been like had it been partially filled with maria material. The surface of Cassini no longer bears the tranquil smoothness of Archimedes and Plato: major upheavals resulting in two sizeable craters have mutilated it, and, while there can be no doubt that this feature belongs to the older generation of inundated craters, the more recent scars, with their own local ray systems, make it impossible to trace Aristillian rays across it. Thus we can deduce the sequence of some lunar events; and this is a necessary prelude to the formidable task of arranging them according to their real age. Nevertheless, the science and principles of geology provide firm beach-heads from which great advances in selenological knowledge will come in the years ahead.

Starting from the region of Copernicus, the eye is attracted north-east to Eratosthenes where commences, humbly at first, the long curved range of the lunar Apennines that form the south-eastern boundary of the Mare Imbrium. This is an impressive range characterized by towering peaks rising high above the

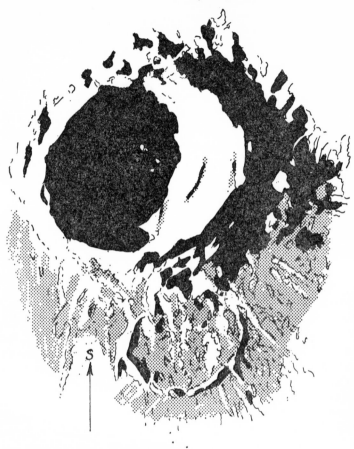

FIG. 19. Aristillus (top) contains far more shadow than the shallow ghost crater on its northern ramparts. It is easy to see, under these lighting conditions, that the latter is very shallow compared to Aristillus.

Mare Imbrium to 16,000 feet and one rocky massif that exceeds 18,000 feet has become a monument to Christopher Huyghens (1629–95), a celebrated Dutch philosopher who was the first to suggest the wave motion of light. By measuring the lengths of the shadows falling on the Mare one may successfully calculate the heights of the mountains casting them. It is more than likely that even loftier peaks exist in the Apennine Range, but, if they are surrounded by neighbouring mountains, it is difficult to measure their shadows: thus they remain undetected. Eventually, after some 400 miles, these mountains—like those in the Irish song—"sweep down to the sea", or more precisely to the Straits mentioned earlier, and for about 40 miles the surface is fairly featureless. An observer standing on Cape Fresnel, the northernmost peak of the Apennines, would be able to see right across the Straits to the Caucasus Mountains which are of the same broken nature as those that have been described. The reader, by studying Antonín Rukl's detailed lunar chart in this volume, will gain far more information about these features than could possibly be given in the text. The Caucasus Range might almost be regarded as a 200-mile-long extension of the Apennines, were it not for the gap separating them, and even this is suggestive of a great flow of maria material that swept out of the younger Mare Serenitatis, carrying everything before it, including great mountain masses. The author hastens to emphasize that this is what the appearance suggests, and his estimate of the youthfulness of the Mare Serenitatis is based solely on the number of large craters within it: in very general terms, most astronomers agree that the larger the crater is the older it is likely to be. A glance at Serenitatis shows that it is devoid of craters greater than about 10 miles in diameter, while, on the other side of the Straits, the Mare Imbrium, as we have already seen, contains several very large circular formations. As well as this, Serenitatis is smaller than Imbrium and so obeys the rough-and-ready rules relating the ages and sizes of craters, if indeed this means anything at all when applied to lunar seas. It seems very likely that the Caucasus Mountains once linked up with the Apennines, and perhaps some of the mountains disappeared under the lava-flows of the Sea of Serenity; however, the situation regarding this and other lunar mysteries is not likely to improve until some of the theories are replaced by solid facts. Before leaving the Causacus Mountains, we should note that this range contains mountains that rise to the same height as some of the Apenninian peaks, and at least one approaches 20,000 feet, from which an observer would have a horizon of 70 miles that would permit him to see parts of both maria in the same vista.

Less rugged are the lunar Alps that extend north-west from the Caucasus Mountains to provide a north-eastern border to the Mare Imbrium. These, like the Apennines, are higher to the west, and if the Mare Imbrium were formed by a cataclysmic mechanism similar to that which moulded the craters and ringed plains, this type of mountain construction, giving an abrupt and lofty perimeter to the plain and gradually sloping away downwards to merge with other maria areas, would tend to strengthen the argument. On the Earth, one can find mountainous areas that show the same characteristics—the Pyrenees, for example, where the author has spent a great deal of time in recent years, rise precipitously to more than 11,000 feet to form the Franco–Spanish frontier, and having achieved this, they fall very slowly again across northern Spain: certainly most geologists would not advocate a common origin for lunar and terrestrial mountains.

The Alpine peaks are generally of the order of 6000 to 8000 feet in height, but here and there, along the Imbrium shores, higher massifs ascend to about 12,000 feet. As might be expected, one such peak is called Mont Blanc after its French Alpine namesake. To the north-east, the lunar Alps lose their mountainous character and degenerate into the form of striated and irregular ridges of macro-rubble generously bespattered with small craters and craterlets. Cutting through the centre of this chaos is the 80-mile-long Alpine Valley which has become a popular object to observe with modest telescopes, but a large instrument will sometimes show the narrow valley or cleft that runs along the centre of the Valley. All sorts of theories have been invoked in attempts to account for the formation of a valley that commences in an Imbrium bay half-way between Cassini and Plato, and which cuts north-east, with varying widths of up to 5 or 6 miles, before fading away near the southern shores of Mare Frigoris. One idea involved a massive low-level high-speed missile that grazed across the Alps, leaving a giant furrow behind it. It is probable that the presence of the Alpine Valley is associated with a surface weakness that caused faulting and lineal and lateral movements of the lunar crust, and there is plenty of evidence to support this viewpoint because there are many more grooves and furrows in all four quadrants of the Moon, and large numbers of these are lined up parallel to each other, while other families with different orientations cut across them in various directions. The Alpine Valley just happens to be a conspicuous wrinkle, a sign of the selenological senility of a face that has etched upon it the ravages of $4\frac{1}{2}$ thousand million years.

If we draw a line south from the western tip of Archimedes until it reaches the lunar Apennines, and another through Autolycus to the Serenitatis/Imbrium Straits, we enclose an area that has its share of isolated, cruciform peaks similar to Piton, and, at least, one prominent ghost crater and numerous small craterlets. In addition, in the crumbly area immediately south of Archimedes one can trace several parallel ridges and shallow gouges that extend south-eastwards until they get lost in the overall confusion of the Apennine Range. Some of them in fact do appear to cross the Range itself, but about 20 miles before reaching the Apennines, another system consisting of several groove-like valleys, running parallel to the Range, cuts the former system almost at right angles. And yet, when the selenologist thinks of lunar valleys and rilles, he does not usually conjure up visions of these particular systems, for the Imbrium Plain, for some obscure reason, is virtually free of classical examples of this type of feature.

Let us make our way south-south-east from Archimedes, scaling the steep "seaward" scarps of the Apennines that hide the gentler descent ever southwards to the Mare Vaporum, where there is little to interest us until we reach its south-eastern shore. It is here that we discover one of the most surprising features of the lunar surface, the Hyginus Rille (see Fig. 20), that consists of two long reasonably linear valleys emanating from a common origin—the small Hyginus crater. Their general configuration resembles two clock-hands indicating the time of 10 minutes to 4: the crater occupies the position of the spindles in the centre. The "hour-hand" valley is some 60 miles in length, and little more than 2 miles across at its widest, and there are at least 7 crateriferous swellings along it, indicating its endogenic or internal

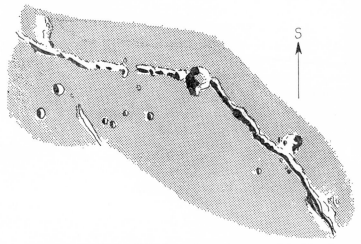

Fig. 20. The Hyginus Rille situated near the centre of the Moon's disc is one of the most prominent and enigmatic of lunar features.

origin. The "minute-hand" is rather more than 70 miles long and it preserves a greater constancy of width, averaging about 1½ miles most of the way. Unlike the other, however, this hand seems to suffer an interruption about 10 miles east of Hyginus: at this point the valley stops, and, after some 3 miles of semi-normal maria surface, it recommences, without deviation, as though nothing had halted it in the first place. Between this interruption and Hyginus there are one or two crater-like swellings similar to those in the hour-hand.

A small telescope will reveal the Hyginus Rille and the prominent Ariadaeus Rille that commences a few miles north of where the eastern hand of the Hyginus system ceases. This rille runs parallel to the direction of the minute-hand for about 150 miles, but, again, not without interruptions in the shape of compact masses of rocks of almost mountainous dimensions that in some cases are associated with rocky protuberances on both sides of the rille. Perhaps even more curious is the manner in which the western half of the rille becomes shallower to the east until it merges with the normal lunar surface, while immediately north, with no more than a low narrow ridge in between, a second valley starts and continues east, once more in the same direction. Fifteen miles before it finishes it throws off a branch that progresses south for 20 miles by which distance it has narrowed into nothingness.

Having ascertained some of the linear dimensions of these extensive systems, the next question to ask is: "How deep are they?" In earlier works there was a tendency to regard these valleys as cracks, and many of the older illustrations showed them as sharp-edged and evidently "bottomless" abysses, but, in point of fact, nothing is farther from the truth. These valleys are shallow linear depressions bounded by gently rounded banks and their depths are of the order of a few hundred yards at the most. If, by some invocation of the Satanic powers, the 250-mile-long Grand Canyon were uprooted from Arizona and transplanted on the surface of the Moon this indeed would be a far more dramatic object to observe through the telescope.

South of the Hyginus Rille is a prominent system of narrower valleys, collectively described as the Triesnecker Clefts (see Fig. 21). There is little doubt that all these three apparently isolated systems are part of one very extensive system that covers many hundreds of square miles of the lunar crust. The origin of the system is a few miles east of the 14-mile-diameter Triesnecker crater that bears the name of an eighteenth-century Austrian astronomer. It is difficult enough to describe this system, but the main features can be traced, approximately, using again our well-worn clock-face. This time we have to imagine spidery clock-hands indicating 5 minutes to 7, but, in addition, there are other hands, one of which radiates from the centre to a point half-way between 6 and

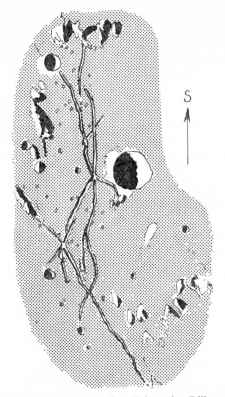

S

FIG. 21. The chief components of the Triesnecker Rille system are indicated in this diagram. Undoubtedly there are many smaller valleys that cannot be shown that may also link up with the Hyginus and Ariadaeus systems to the north. Triesnecker, the only large crater in the whole area, is close to the centre of the Moon's disc.

7: another points straight at 12, but this is crossed by a branch that stems from the 40-mile minute-hand. At the 7 position the 20-mile hour-hand narrows and fills up, but it is replaced immediately by a 10-mile extension that precedes another, originating from which three other clefts radiate, making, with the fourth, a scissor-like pattern. At this point the author advises the reader to examine Fig. 21.

The Triesnecker Clefts are best observed at around the time of first and last quarters when they are illuminated by grazing sunlight, for under a high Sun they disappear altogether. These valleys are about 1 mile in width, and to the author they have represented something of a challenge. Some few years ago a 6-inch reflecting telescope was used to photograph the Moon, and, often, images of the Hyginus and Ariadaeus systems were obtained. Despite these modest successes the author never succeeded in photographing the Triesnecker Clefts, although they were plainly discernible through the eyepiece.

Let us leave behind us these systems of rilles, valleys and clefts, and head south across the Sinus Medii and the 50-mile irregular Flammarion, which is not nearly so celebrated as the 6-mile-diameter Mösting A embedded in its western walls. We have already noted that clefts can disappear according to the prevailing illumination on the lunar surface: the same is true of craters; even giant craters such as Clavius perform disappearing tricks, particularly at full Moon, when the relief, normally emphasized by the shadows, is absent. Before photography became the chief weapon in the astronomer's armoury—this takes us back about 100 years —micrometric measurements had to be performed directly upon the lunar image as it appeared to the observer at his telescope, and one of the tasks, sometimes laboriously carried out in freezing conditions, was that of measuring the distances of points around the edge of the disc against a common point near the centre. Mösting A, because of its prominence at all phases, was chosen as the standard point, but we should spare a thought for the astronomers who dedicated their lives to a problem that has only become soluble with the advent of the electronic computer. This is the task of determining by how much the shape of the Moon differs from a sphere. Originally this study was of academic interest only; within the last 5 years it has become an important—even urgent— problem that has to be solved before accurate contoured charts can be made of the lunar surface.

Skirting west of Ptolemeus, and taking only a passing glance at Alphonsus to which we shall return later, we eventually arrive at the eastern shores of the Mare Nubium, which bears upon its surface one of the strangest linear features that is without equal in any other part of the visible lunar hemisphere. This is the Straight Wall (see Fig. 22) which is orientated not quite parallel to the

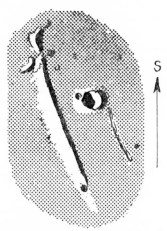

S

Fig. 22. The Straight Wall (60 miles long) is a fault in the lunar crust. The higher level to the east is left unshaded in the figure. Note the parallel valley running north from Birt.

central meridian. Its southern or upper end on our inverted lunar chart points east of south like a clock minute-hand that has about 5 minutes to go before registering the hour.

Starting at the northern end, in the vicinity of a small but conspicuous crater, we can travel about 60 miles, either along the top of the wall or along the base. A good deal depends on whether the traveller prefers to look upwards at this 800–1000-foot feature, or whether he wishes to sample the view from the top. In fact it does not matter very much if he prefers to take the high road or the low road for, apart from the Straight Wall itself, there is nothing very dramatic to claim his attention. Neither route will bring him to a crater larger than that in Arizona.

Early astronomers used their imaginations to supplement the imperfections of their telescopes, and some were convinced that the Straight Wall was not a natural feature of the Moon, but something erected by intelligent beings for a mysterious purpose. Others regarded it as a natural feature but endowed it with cliff-like properties, and we can still turn back to artists' impressions showing unscalable, perpendicular and lofty rock-faces diminishing into the distance and eventually curving way beyond the lunar horizon. If this were really the true state of affairs, and remembering that the so-called cliff-face is turned to the west and that its position is not far from the central lunar meridian, our terrestrial vantage-point should yield us a view not unlike that obtained by an observer in a balloon tethered above a vertical cliff. Such a person would see little or nothing of the face of the cliff. In the case of the Straight Wall the fact is, however, that we do, and when the Sun illuminates this face, it becomes brighter than its surroundings, and one may then measure its apparent width, which is approximately 2·5 kilometres or a little more than $1\frac{1}{2}$ miles. Knowing the height, we can work out the slope, and this yields a gradient of about one in nine which is not only easily scalable on foot, but is a gradient encountered very often by the motorist: many roads are steeper than this.

Powerful telescopes reveal imperfections and irregularities and few experts doubt that the Straight Wall is a selenological fault that, as the result of the release of internal pressures, produced an abrupt change in level of the floor of what was formerly a ringed plain of about 120 miles in diameter. The eastern ramparts of this plain are easily discernible, while wrinkle ridges to the south-west hint at western walls that have been almost obliterated by intrusions of maria material from the adjacent Mare Nubium. To the south, the Straight Wall is halted by a 20-mile serrated mountain ridge of no great height, and, farther south again, the regular curve of the Stag's Horn Mountains deflects the south-going line of the wall round to the south-west. These mountains supply a "sword-handle" to the "blade" formed by the Straight Wall, and in doing so they ascend to about 2000 feet.

A few miles west of the centre of the Straight Wall is a crater of about 8 miles in diameter which is called Birt, after a well-known nineteenth-century observer. On its south-eastern rampart, a small 2-mile crater has spoiled the symmetry of its walls, but there is nothing very extraordinary about this, for prodigious numbers of lunar craters are related in this manner; in fact, if we were specifically hunting for such features, there is a finer example of three interrelated craters only 35 miles east of the Wall. The biggest is 28 miles across, and this is inroaded to the north-west by one of 10 miles, and intruding into the north-west wall of the latter is the youngest of the trio, which is about 5 miles across. The largest of this group is called Thebit, in honour of a Persian astronomer who lived more than a thousand years ago. However, with this short excursion completed, we return to the environs of Birt, not to re-examine what is after all a fairly ordinary type of structure, but to regard the shallow valley that commences closely west of it. Starting from what appears to be a small crater, it describes a gently curving arc to the north-north-west for 28 miles before terminating in another elongated crater-like pit. The curvature of this valley is gentle enough to permit the valley to be described as running parallel to the Straight Wall, and there is good reason to suppose that it too is a sign of crustal weakening.

Having studied the photographs and the chart, the reader will realize that our brief appraisals of several interesting lunar objects have merely scratched the surface of an enormous subject, for which we cannot possibly find sufficient space in a descriptive volume of this size. We could discuss at some length the wired Wargentin formation (see Fig. 23) which can be found close to the limb at about 2 o'clock in quadrant 3. This 54-mile-diameter object is evidently a ringed plain of the Archimedean type that by some mysterious means was filled almost to the top of its ramparts with maria material, and, instead of it draining away again, it gives the impression of having solidified *in situ*. Thus the smooth floor of Wargentin is a few thousand feet above its very broken and irregular external environment and remains a unique and baffling example of lunar features that do not seem to have abided by the rules. Indeed if we could read correctly the secrets of the Wargentin rocks we would be well along the road of under-

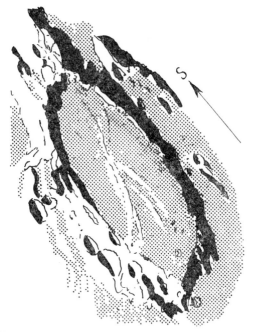

Fig. 23. When selenologists understand the nature of the 54-mile Wargentin formation, near the south-west limb of quadrant 3, they will have solved the secrets of one of the most mysterious objects on the Moon.

standing and interpreting the forces that twisted and puckered the face of the infant Moon.

From Wargentin the eye can travel round the limb to the 12 o'clock position, then straight down through the centre of the disc in the direction of 6 o'clock whence it will pass close to the Imbrium/Serenitatis Straits. A few miles east of these the eye will not be arrested but will nevertheless see a small crater in the Mare Serenitatis that is called Linné. Since this crater is not very much larger than the terrestrial one in Arizona the reader might well wonder why his attention has been drawn to it, and the author hastens to explain that it is not because of its $1\frac{1}{2}$ mile diameter— there are countless thousands of similar craters in all four quadrants of the visible surface and there are doubtless many thousands more on the face that we cannot see from the Earth. To be sure Linné cannot lay claim to any distinction arising from dimensional disparities: it is a very ordinary crater and, to this day, few observers would have taken much notice of it had it not been a subject of controversy during the latter half of the nineteenth century. The measurements of Lohrmann and Mädler made during the first half of the nineteenth century yielded a diameter of about 5 miles for this crater. Later, Schmidt, another well-known observer of the Moon, pointed out a discrepancy that suggested that either a change had taken place in the diameter of Linné or that the earlier records were not to be trusted. The author can envisage a set of circumstances in which the undermined ramparts of a small crater might collapse to produce a larger one—there is, of course, no evidence of this process happening on the Moon—but it is difficult to imagine how a 5-mile diameter could "stop-down", using photographic terminology, to only $1\frac{1}{2}$ miles. The real explanation probably stems from the fact that Linné occupies the centre of a whitish patch of about 5 miles diameter in Mare Serenitatis and it seems most likely that the vital measurements were made across the patch rather than the crater. Certainly during the fuller phases of the Moon most craters take on bright appearances and this, in the case of Linné, may have deceived the earlier observers with their small telescopes.

As for the problem as to whether structural changes still occur in the lunar crustal rocks—we say "still" because the face of the Moon displays the record of a cataclysmic past, and there may be occasional outbursts of feeble activity at the present time— all that can be said is that no well-confirmed evidence has been produced. At the same time an observer looking back to the

Earth from the lunar surface would see nothing of the geological contortions that shape the Earth, so if we apply the same argument to the Moon there may well be considerable activity taking place but on a scale that defies detection from a distance of 240,000 miles. Our search for the typical and the unusual has revealed a great variety of lunar features; and considerable space, if it were available, could be devoted to descriptions of special features like the 62-mile-diameter Posidonius or its slightly smaller brother, the 55-mile-diameter Gassendi. These low-walled ringed plains are well separated from each other and they occupy positions on the northern shores of Mare Serenitatis and the Mare Humorum respectively (see Lunar chart, p. 82, 83). These give every appearance of being "missing links" between the Wargentin-type and the Archimedes-type formations, and they are characterized by the complicated systems of ridges and rilles that cut across their uneven floors. Or again, a glance at the limb area at about 10 o'clock in quadrant 4 will reveal the vast 100-mile Petavius which is described as a ringed plain but really possesses features that we generally associate with craters plus one additional and interesting feature that makes Petavius unique. This is the straight and shallow valley that connects the serrated central peaks to the south-west wall of the formation. There can be little doubt that this valley is the result of the faulting or collapsing of the lunar surface, and this is a very fine example of the result of a process that has played a major part in lunar sculpture.

Most of the objects visited so far have been prominent; and adjectives like vast, enormous, grand, etc., have been employed to describe them. However, there are other features that are inconspicuous and remain hidden even under high solar illumination. In fact it is only when the grazing rays of the Sun stretch across the melancholy early morning or late afternoon landscapes of the Moon that these objects, the lunar *domes*, come into prominence. Let us discard, at once, the notion of shapes like observatory domes, or those that embellish the churches and mosques of many of the world's great capitals. Lunar domes do not deserve the description that the name implies, for they are little more than low convexities on the smooth lunar plains. Some of them are quite irregular, while others display almost lens-like symmetry. Some members of the family, and this is a fairly typical characteristic, possess rimless depressions on summits that rise no more than a few hundred yards above the surrounding maria surface. In spite of their modest heights their diameters by comparison are often large, and 10 miles represents a typical value and, from this, we find that the slopes are of the order of 1° or 2°—the sort of slope that a cyclist might scale without being aware of its existence.

Lunar domes often occur in groups, and some of the best known are close to the craters Milichius and Hortensius, west of Copernicus, where 11 have been detected. Another fine pair occupy positions in the western Mare Tranquillitatis between the crater Arago and the eastern end of the Ariadaeus Rille. Many well-known domes take their names from the craters with which they are closely associated; thus we have the Cauchy and Kies domes in eastern Tranquillitatis and western Mare Nubium respectively, and there are a few more, scattered mostly in the Imbrian and Procellarian plains.

Almost as strange as themselves are some of the theories of evolution that have been postulated, and, in some cases, vehemently defended by their protagonists; thus it is small wonder that the lunar domes have become subjects of some speculation in recent years. There are a few ideas that are interesting in themselves because of their originality. One that is fairly popular at the time of writing draws a parallel between lunar domes and terrestrial laccoliths, the latter being subsurface cavities filled originally with molten rock that forced the comparatively thin rocky lids upwards to form domes. Selenologists, it seems, always feel more secure if they can tether their theories to geological moorings, and it has not escaped their attention that nature uses ice, instead of magma, to produce similar doming of the rocks in the Arctic and Antarctic regions of the Earth. We have therefore to consider the possibility that lunar ice may be present in the subsurface rocks of the Moon and that it may exert upward pressures on the crustal rocks to produce the doming that we see through our telescopes. It has been calculated by Watson, Murray and Brown that lunar ice, once formed, could remain protected for thousands of years away from the warming solar rays by a comparatively thin insulating layer of the lunar crust. How the ice gets there in the first instance poses something of a difficulty for, if the birth of the Moon were a hot one, all original water would have been boiled off into space. Alternatively, if the lunar globe suffered a cool genesis and was built up gradually by the accretion of dust, rocks and even small asteroids, the whole science of selenology could be placed on a firmer foundation, for the accretion process still operates, though at a rate that does not greatly influence the larger bodies of the solar system. Meteoritic materials that fall upon the Earth have been collected and submitted to chemical analysis, and there is no reason to suppose that those that have fallen on the Moon are any different in composition from those that occupy the shelves of the British Museum. In addition to the normal chemical content of the stoney chondritic meteorites, radioactive isotopes of potassium, thorium and uranium (K^{40}, Th^{232}, U^{235}, U^{235}) have been detected in small amounts and H. Urey has suggested that these would tend to heat the body containing them, and, if the Moon is composed of this material, the implication is that the Moon is still heating up and not cooling down. We can therefore envisage a mechanism that warms the internal rocks of the Moon to drive out the small traces of water trapped within them. This water escapes as vapour that continues to move towards the surface until it reaches a depth where the temperature is low enough to freeze it into ice which accumulates and forces up the rock strata above it. Interesting as this theory is, there are many difficulties and unknown factors and, in view of the findings of the space-probes Lunik 9 and Surveyor 1, there now seems to be a resurgence of the theories relying on lunar vulcanism, and the result of this swing is to strengthen the arguments favouring the formation of lunar laccolithic structures by intrusions of molten rock or magma.

Other investigators have put forward other variations on similar themes, and we do not have to delve far into the literature before we encounter the gas-bubble theory in which the upward forces are generated by gas pressure from below the surface. This does not seem to be quite as simple to set up, for, to have a sub-surface cavity, at no great depth below the lunar surface, filled with gas under sufficient pressure to distort the rocks above demands a nice balance of the physical factors involved. So as to make this mechanism work we need a blanket of rock uniform in density and thickness spread over, say, 100 square miles of the lunar surface and, when the gas pressure increases to force it upwards, it must remain in one sheet without fracturing. Any crack or fault would release the entombed gases and it is more than likely that once the process of arching had commenced the upper rock layer would suffer multi-fracturing and the gases would rapidly escape into space. The gas-bubble theory is attributed to Robert Hooke, a contemporary of Isaac Newton, who introduced it to explain the formation of lunar craters and there may well be strong physical connections between the formations of craters and domes.

Without involving lunar ice or gas our safest course is to consider the crater- and dome-forming mechanism as one that employs magmatic intrusions into cavities of the subsurface rocks. We can imagine a solid cylinder of viscous rock pushing up the surface into a dome, and, if this releases the pressure from down below and the magma solidifies *in situ*, a permanent dome may be formed. On the other hand, let us suppose that the column of magma descends again after forming the lunar dome—what happens to the newly formed structure? Well, it is fairly obvious that the dome cannot remain in its elevated position, and it seems logical to expect the dome to collapse after the pressure has been removed. If the downward descent of the magmatic cylinder is sufficient the dome may collapse to form a depression similar to a terrestrial caldera which may be regarded as a member of the crater family. It seems very likely that this type of process has played a large part in moulding the lunar surface features that we see so clearly through our telescopes, but, as with all other lunar processes, there are many unknown factors and we may have to wait a few more years before the true state of affairs can be assessed.

CHAPTER 4

The Nature of the Lunar Surface

IT IS often said that an aircraft, a space vehicle or even a computer is out of date before it leaves the designer's drawing-board. To a lesser degree the same can be said for a book dealing with a subject as topical as the Moon, for the scientific panorama changes continuously and no one can tell what a new day holds in store or what fresh horizons will be opened up. In recent months the pace of lunar probing has increased to such an extent that it is difficult to present an up-to-date account of the results and it is now becoming such a refined art that the author would not be exercising his imagination too vividly if he asserted that, by the time this book is published, packages of measuring instruments will have been soft-landed on the lunar surface and programmed to perform analytical studies of the lunar rocks and to transmit the data back to Earth. Although the pattern of future events can be dimly discerned up to the time of the first manned landing, the surprises and jolts to respected ideas that lie in store for us cannot be truly assessed unless we know something about the earlier theories and researches that were made before the commencement of the astronautical era.

Fortunately we do not have to travel too far back in time, for most of the more meaningful lunar observations have taken place during the last century. Earlier, before the advent of the spectrometer and the photographic plate, observations of the Moon were confined to visual studies undertaken by a dedicated handful of enthusiasts whose long nocturnal vigils at the telescopes were completely unknown to a non-caring populace. These observers made charts, measured distances, and calculated the heights of mountains and crater rims by methods that are still in use at the present time. Such was the message of moonlight to the few who achieved so much.

Apart from the observational and topographical work, moonlight itself provides an interesting modern line of study. Basically the light that reaches us from the Moon is reflected and scattered sunlight. It we point a simple spectroscope at the Moon we shall see the same configuration of Fraunhöfer lines as we see in the solar spectrum. However, not all of the solar light is reflected or scattered: some of it is absorbed by the lunar rocks, and with more elaborate equipment it is possible to demonstrate that moonlight is redder than sunlight. There are other differences, too, for there is a growing body of opinion that supports a hypothesis that was first proposed by F. Link in the 1930's that the Moon luminesces when the energetic ultra-violet and corpuscular radiations of the Sun strike the rocks. These phenomena are very localized and their light only amounts to a few per cent of the totals emitted from given areas—the search for transient colorations is important because the causes are not known and they cannot be ignored lest they lurk to trap the unwary astronaut.

Even with the latest sophisticated photometric equipment the astronomer does not find it easy to measure accurately the intensities of lunar colours, and it is even more difficult for him to relate his reduced values to those of other investigators. Phase angle, defined as the difference between the selenographic longitude of the Sun's centre and that of the observer, plays a dominant role in determining the quantity of moonlight that is available for measurement. Librational effects, causing apparent lengthening and foreshortening of lunar features, also bring lighter and darker areas into view from the averted hemisphere. A further complication arises as a result of the presence of the Earth's atmosphere and before the lunar photometrist can place any reliance upon his deductions he must also measure the fluxes of certain stars that are known to possess constant outputs of light. These become his standards, and by alternating his measurements between the Moon and such stars during an observational session he can collect information that will permit him to assess the atmospheric absorptions as functions of wavelengths, whence he can apply them to correct his lunar measurements.

With the landing of the Russian Lunik 9 on the lunar surface we entered a new era for, up to that moment, moonlight had been our only link with the "queen of the night". And not only with the Moon—light arriving on the Earth from points in the Universe many millions of times more distant than our satellite can be submitted to several standard forms of analysis that will reveal certain properties of the light that in turn will tell us something about the physical nature of the body from which the light emanates.

When Lunik 9 started to transmit its pictures of the lunar surface back to the Earth in the early morning hours of 4th February, 1966 it demolished a number of currently and widely held theories concerning the small-scale structure of the lunar surface, but, at the same time, it upheld others that were based on optical and radio methods. Among the former were dust theories based on quite reasonable assumptions that the Moon had been behaving, throughout it long history, like a giant celestial vacuum cleaner and had swept up huge quantities of cosmic dust and debris by its own gravitational attraction. In addition to the accretion of interplanetary dust theories we must also include those that asserted that dust must also be present on the lunar surface as a result of the crater-forming processes. This, again, is a reasonable assumption, for many large craters possess extensive ray systems in which one may search for and find hundreds of secondary craterlets. The fact that terrestrial experiments with atom-bomb craters have produced similar effects underlines the theory that, by whatever means—externally or internally—a large crater is formed by explosive forces that excavate and eject all the material away from the crater. Thus secondary craters are made by the impact of large boulders and debris, and palls of dust are stirred that settle into the ray systems we see through our telescopes. After such an explosion all dust and debris that exceeds a velocity of $1\frac{1}{2}$ miles per second escapes into space and from this we conclude that the ray material may have been travelling at much slower speeds than this, and, if so, some of it should still be loose and dusty and not welded or compacted. Lunik 9 did not soft-land in a ray area so the question is still an open one at the time of writing.

An interesting theory was propounded some years ago by T. Gold, who suggested that the maria regions of the Moon were really composed of dust deposits of kilometre depths and that the dust had flowed on electrostatic cushions from the highlands to the lowlands. The essence of the flow mechanism can be understood if we consider two microscopic dust grains carrying electrical charges of the same polarity—perhaps charged-up pith balls hanging from silken threads in a school laboratory will awaken memories for some readers—either way the dust grains or the pith balls will repel each other. If the upper layer of the lunar surface is charged we can appreciate that microscopic dust-grains, carrying like charges, will not settle or even touch the surface below but will glide downhill like miniature hovercraft until the lateral movement is arrested by some larger fragment of rock. This, in fact, seems to be one of the problems with Gold's transport mechanism: it works well with dust of micron dimensions—this phenomenon has been tested in physical laboratories—but not with larger particles. On the other hand, we cannot rule out entirely the possibility that there may be localized areas of the lunar surface where dust migration of this type occurs; but it is most unlikely that such movements could ever be detected from the Earth. In the original hypothesis Gold stated that if the thickness of the dust on the maria increases in depth by as much as 1 micron (1/1000 millimetre) per year, this would be sufficient to account for dust deposits of perhaps a few kilometres in depth that had drifted to the lowland areas over the 4,500,000,000 years of the Moon's existence. This large volume of dust, according to the theory, has its origin in mountains and crater walls that were eroded by micrometeoritic showers and corpuscular radiation from the Sun.

At the time of writing this little volume there have been only two soft-landings on the lunar surface*—Lunik 9 and the American Surveyor. Both landed in the maria areas and, from what has so far been published, it appears that each instrument televised surface areas where no dust could be detected. Photographs, whether obtained by television or ordinary photography, do not in themselves furnish sufficient proof for us to assert authoritatively that dust does not exist on the Moon, and we cannot as yet dismiss the possibility of considerable quantities being present in the cracks and crevices of the two small samples of a total surface of about 14,000,000 square miles. Also it would be unwise for us to conclude that all of the great lunar plains or maria are similarly composed, although it must be conceded that the areas selected for the soft-landings appear to be very typical of the maria regions. Using a terrestrial analogy, if a visitor from a distant planet were to set foot on the sands of the Sahara Desert, he might be forgiven for believing that the rest of the Earth's surface was of a sandy composition, although we know that this is very far from the mark.

Let us look more closely at the mechanisms that demand of us the acceptance that micrometeoritic dusts fall upon the surface of the Moon. Firstly, the Earth and Moon are so closely linked gravitationally that they occupy, to all intents and purposes, the same part of interplanetary space—a separation of 240,000 miles is practically nothing at all on the cosmic scale. We may therefore conclude that any extraterrestrial dust showers that are incident on the Earth are also falling simultaneously on the Moon, and scientists, using satellite-borne instruments and other techniques, are now able to state with some precision the magnitude of the infall of micrometeoritic material in the Earth–Moon environs. The results of such analyses have hinted at accretion rates of around 5 million tons per year for the whole terrestrial globe, and, if this seems to be a large volume of dust, remember that it has to be shared out between all of the 196,836,000 square miles of the Earth's surface, of which only 55,786,000 square miles are land. If we make certain assumptions—not necessarily correct ones—in the case of the Moon, firstly that the infall is about 1 %

* See revised list, p. 161

of the Earth's and that it has been constant for 4·5 aeons (4·5 × 10⁹ years)—the estimated age of the Moon—we can then calculate the approximate thickness of meteoric material that should now be present on the lunar surface. Assuming an accretion rate of 50,000 tons per year and an average density of 6 grams per cubic centimetre, which is a figure given for stony-iron meteorites, we eventually conclude that each square yard of the Moon's surface is covered with 5 tons of accreted material to an average depth of about 5 yards.

Now for the fallacies. The above conclusions are based on premises that are impossible to confirm. Firstly, we just do not know if the present accretion rate bears any similarity to that of even a few thousand years ago—let alone aeons. Secondly, it is currently held that each high-speed impact of meteoritic material releases sufficient energy to accelerate fragments of the existing lunar surface to escape velocity and, as we have already noted, such material leaves the Moon for all time. If this theory fits the facts, the Moon, instead of gaining, may actually be losing mass by meteoritic infall. Notwithstanding this, if each impact creates an exploding and expanding shell of pulverized material, only a fraction of this will leave the Moon entirely: the rest will expend its energy within the lunar rocks and one of the end-products may be just more dust. A number of investigators have attempted to estimate by indirect methods the sizes of the dust-grains that each would expect to find on the Moon and there has been some measure of agreement in their results. These assessments have revealed that lunar dust grains ought to lie in the 1–100 micron (1/1000 – 1/10 millimetre) range with particular emphasis on the 5–60 micron (5/1000–6/100 millimetre) sizes. Just how this information matches up to the discoveries made by the Lunik 9 and the Surveyor will be reviewed in a later chapter—our task at the moment is to provide the background scenery in front of which the modern drama of lunar exploration may be enacted.

Thus we have no direct information as to whether the Moon is gaining or losing mass by micrometeoritic infall and, although the Earth is subjected to the same bombardment from interplanetary space, the welcome presence of our atmosphere denies us the opportunity of performing the practical experiments that would enable us to discover the true nature of the process. Small fragments of metal and rock entering the atmosphere at meteoric speeds of 10 – 20 miles per second are vaporized long before they can penetrate to ground-level.

In most sciences and until reliable facts are discovered, there are as likely to be as many theories as theorists: the same is no less true of lunar studies and, to avoid what might be interpreted as bias on the part of the author in favour of the lunar dust theories, we now pass on to others that postulate the absence of dust. F. L. Whipple, like Gold, presented his theory in 1959 and evoked a mechanism that also involved the effects of solar radiation—this time protons—on molecules of heavier gases from the interplanetary medium plus the vaporized gases released from micrometeoritic impacts. He concluded that the net result would be to weld the dust-grains into a low-density, semiporous, sponge-like solid that would be stronger than a dust surface, but by no means as unyielding as terrestrial sedimentary rocks. As we shall observe later on, this description tallies very well with what we now know about the lunar surface after the soft-landings. Whipple also asserted that loose dust on the Moon is practically non-existent because the relatively good electrical conduction of the interplanetary medium, in contact with the lunar surface, quickly removes strong surface static charges. The interplanetary medium may here be regarded as a tenuous, all-enveloping extension of the solar atmosphere. Whipple's findings are supported by those of other investigators, including S. F. Singer and E. H. Walker, who condemn the electrostatic dust transport mechanism but point out that meteoritic impacts can contribute to dust production and that this material will tend to settle in crevices and on mountain slopes rather than in the smooth marial areas.

In the last decade attempts have been made to test out some of the theories by simulating lunar environmental conditions in the laboratory, and a good deal of study is being directed at problems associated with lunar soil mechanics with special emphasis upon those relating to the behaviour of powders in high-vacuum. Such experiments involve the placing of powders inside chambers that are afterwards sealed and evacuated. Not least of the problems is how to get the air molecules out of the powders for, even after hours of pumping, air continues to be released from such substances, and lunar conditions cannot be realized until all gases have been exhausted. Many experiments have been completed and considerable progress has been made in understanding how powders adhere to each other in airless environments, as well as the part played by gravitational forces and the effects of corpuscular radiation. It is also possible these days to accelerate small material particles and aim them at rock specimens so as to simulate hypervelocity meteoritic impacts. All of these studies and many others besides yield information that permit us to know more about the possible nature of the surface of our only natural satellite; but we must not stray too far from our original path.

As we have already noted, only a brief decade ago man was completely earthbound and had no alternative but to conduct all his astronomical researches from ground-based observatories. In those days his strongest weapons were the telescope, the camera, the spectrograph, the polarimeter and the photometer; and all of these have played their part and still continue to do so.

To the visual observer the largest telescopes will reveal circular lunar objects down to about 100 yards in diameter, and the same instrument can reveal the presence of linear objects such as rilles and clefts that are narrower than this. Nothing relating to the small-scale structure of the surface can be found by such means; hence the dust-versus-solid controversies that have ebbed and flowed during the last few decades. Now it is an unfortunate fact that, while the eye of the observer can be trained to extract all visible information from a small fragment of the lunar image, it is not nearly so effective in examining extended areas of the Moon. This is why the camera, with its ability to record all areas simultaneously, has played such a large part in lunar research in recent years. Notwithstanding this, there are also some disadvantages with the photographic technique that makes it impossible for the camera to match the optical resolution of the human eye and the best lunar photographs taken from Earth-based telescopes reveal circular objects that are about 300–400 yards across.

The most versatile of instruments and the chief weapon of the physicist is without doubt the spectrograph. It is probably true to say that, had it never been discovered, the science of astrophysics would never have broken away from its terrestrial parent. With such a tool the astronomer may compare the spectrum of sunlight to that of moonlight, and, if there are any detectable differences in the nature of the two spectra, these must be due either to surface absorptions or emissions on the Moon or to gaseous absorptions or emissions in the lunar and terrestrial atmospheres. As we shall observe in the next chapter, there are occasional phenomena that take place close to the lunar surface that have been detected by spectrographic means. Attempts have also been made to find spectral absorptions of the lunar crust in the hope that the rocks responsible for the absorptions may be identified with their terrestrial counterparts. Nothing very positive has emerged from this type of work and the results are disappointing. The spectrograph has also been used with some success to detect the luminescence of the lunar rocks. Notwithstanding this, the most reliable results in this research have come from the spectrograph's close relative, the photoelectric scanning spectrometer.

The optical polarization of the lunar surface is a well-known property that, in theory, can lead to an improved knowledge of the microstructure of the lunar surface. Elegantly designed polarimeters have been constructed and used to examine the lunar surface and many readings have been taken. Despite this, the real problem is to interpret the measurements unambiguously before an accurate assessment of the surface granularity characteristics can be made.

One of the most efficient tools for the ground-based observer of the Moon is the photometer which, now that narrow-band coloured filters are available, can also operate as a type of spectrograph. The Moon possesses photometric properties that have puzzled astronomers for a long time. Firstly, if it were a perfectly smooth shiny globe we should see a small specular image of the Sun reflected from its surface during the gibbous and full phases, and if it were smooth but without a shiny surface it would be distinctly brighter in the centre of the disc than at the edges— it would exhibit the phenomenon known generally as "limb darkening". The Moon does not show this effect at all; in fact, near the time of full Moon, all parts of the disc appear to be reflecting uniformly so that a bright area near the centre would be as bright as a limb area of equal albedo. Even more interesting is the knowledge that all lunar areas, regardless of their respective positions on the lunar surface as seen from the Earth, exhibit sharp maxima in reflected solar light intensity at full Moon. Perhaps this last statement should be qualified by reminding the reader that the true full Moons always involve lunar eclipses and that the opposition effect, as it has been called, could not occur under eclipse conditions.

What does this mean? What sort of surface can behave in this way, and why is the albedo—the percentage of reflected light compared to incident light—so small? The brightest spot on the visible lunar hemisphere is the crater Aristarchus that reflects about 18% of the incident light. The darkest areas have 5% albedoes while, for the whole disc, the mean albedo approaches 7%.

Another way to appreciate the albedo idea is to use our imaginations. One of the most efficient diffuse reflectors is magnesium oxide, which is formed when magnesium ribbon is burnt. Let us suppose that we have a globe as large and as distant as the Moon coated with this material, and let us substitute it for the full Moon. The full Moon illumination that lightens our midnight hour is now more than 14 times as bright as the normal full Moon and, if we measure the brightness of this synthetic Moon with a photometer and compare it to that of the real Moon, we should find that the latter amounted to only 7% of the former with its almost perfect reflecting surface. In other words the Moon is a very poor reflector of solar light and may be regarded as an enormous dark grey ball of rock.

B. Hapke of Cornell University, New York, has probably come closer than anyone in postulating the requirements to satisfy a lunar surface of this type. He has pointed out that a material that can backscatter light as strongly as the lunar surface must not only have an extremely porous and open structure, but, and this point he emphasizes, the cavities within it must also be inter-connected. As well as this the rocks must be dark enough to absorb at least 70% of the incident light and they must be opaque —in other words, light must not be transmitted through the substance as in china or glass. Lastly it must possess rougher microsurfaces. Only in a material of this kind can he find the properties he requires to explain this phenomenon. The opposition effect can now be neatly explained on the basis that the incident light and the reflected light use the same entrances in the material. It is easy enough to imagine a parallel situation where a coalminer, wearing his helmet with a lamp attached to it, perceives no shadows cast by the rays of his lamp because, to him, they are always hidden by the objects casting them. Likewise a flashgun fixed to a camera will permit a photographer to record the images of people and objects that are rendered virtually shadowless on the finished photographs. Move the miner's lamp or the flashgun to one side or the other and shadows will appear to the miner, and the flat, startled faces on the photograph will be replaced by others that are contoured by the oblique lighting. It is not so easy, however, to find a terrestrial object that will emulate the optical properties of the lunar surface and, in particular, display the opposition effect. Stacks of earthenware pipes or hollow building bricks supply plenty of cavities and walls, but perhaps the best material that comes to mind is the cellular structure of the hexagonal-holed comb of the honey-bee. With light shining directly into the empty cells there would be strong backscattering towards the source, mainly from the bottom surfaces of the cells. Under other angles of illumination the light would not get deep enough into the cells to illuminate the bottom surfaces, and this would cause a large diminution of the reflected light seen by the observer. Useful as this model is in helping to explain the so-called opposition effect, it fails lamentably to supply the other properties we require, for it is not opaque and neither does it possess rough microsurfaces. Its cellular structure is also too regular and we ought to dismiss immediately any notions concerning a lunar surface composed of anything as regular as honeycomb.

Hapke is by no means the only investigator to propose a lunar surface following this description. Russian astronomers have also been very active in this field, among them A. V. Markov, N. P. Barabashev, V. V. Sharonov and N. N. Sytinskaya, and it is worth while to quote some of the conclusions of the last-named astronomer:

(a) that the lunar surface should consist of an extremely porous, vesicular material;

(b) that it should consist of a loose, sufficiently coherent material that could give sharp/rough structure capable of adhering to the steepest slopes;

(c) that it should have originated in such a manner that its reflectivity is determined by the mineralogical or petrographic composition of rocks situated in the given region.

These results were presented at the International Astronomical Union Symposium No. 14 held in Leningrad in December 1960. It is interesting to note that the first conclusion is not based on the optical properties of the lunar surface, such as were invoked by Hapke, but on the thermal properties. To appreciate this idea we have to imagine a Moon that is not very cold in its interior—by terrestrial standards this is still uncomfortably cold—and, being warmer than its immediate surroundings, this internal heat escapes through the lunar crust and is dissipated in space. Fortunately for the astronomer this radiation occupies much longer wavelengths than the solar radiation reflected by the lunar surface and so it is possible for him to separate and measure the two forms of radiation. When it comes to measuring the radiation from space at observatories on the Earth's surface the main obstacle is the atmosphere, which is quite opaque at some infrared frequencies. We have, as everyone knows, the optical window from about

4000 to 7000 Ångstroms and in addition there are a few others through which the ground-based observer may receive information about the Moon. Thus we may utilize the infrared region of the spectrum where there are windows at 4–6 microns and at 8–13 microns. The region between 25 and 500 microns is completely useless because of its opacity, but it is possible to resume observations in the radio microwave region around 1 millimetre up to, say, 10 metres. In addition, very good results have attended the radar experiments of bouncing radio pulses from the lunar surface in the 8–18-metre wavebands, and by such means scientists have ascertained, not only an accurate determination of the Earth–Moon distance, but have also arrived at a figure for the dielectric constant of the lunar rocks. In this connection the assumption has been made that the radar pulse penetrates the lunar crust to a depth of about one wavelength, so at 18-metre wavelengths it should be possible to learn something about the subsurface rocks some 50 feet below the surface. The value of the deduced lunar dielectric constant is given as approximately 2·7 which is also the value of dry sandy soils on the Earth.

Under lunar eclipse conditions, when the light and heat of the Sun is abruptly cut off and the shadow of the Earth glides across the lunar globe, the surface temperature drops from about 370°K to the vicinity of 140°K which is about + 100° to −130° on the Centigrade scale—in other words from the boiling-point of water at terrestrial sea-level down to temperatures capable of solidifying elements such as chlorine and xenon. At a depth of less than 0·2 centimetre the insulation properties begin to manifest themselves and the amplitude of the heat wave is reduced to about 140°C and it has been confirmed that at depths of 20–30 centimetres (8–12 inches) the subsurface temperatures remain constant at −35°C regardless of whether the Sun is shining on the rocks above or not. In fact the insulation properties of the crustal rocks are so good as to lead some investigators to believe that they are not tightly compacted but highly porous, and that up to about 50% of their volume consists of cavities containing nothing but pure vacuum. This in turn has led other workers to express fears that the lunar surface may not be solid enough to support the weight of heavy space vehicles, and there may have been some substance to these fears because it was reported that Lunik 9 changed its position after landing on the lunar surface.

Some interesting lunar eclipse radiometry in the 10–12 micron band was performed at the Kottamia Observatory in Egypt on 19th December, 1964 by J. M. Saari and R. W. Shorthill of the Boeing Scientific Research Laboratories. They attached a scanning mechanism to the 74-inch reflector and obtained thermal measurements that later indicated that many craters, including Tycho and Dawes, were warmer than the surrounding lunar surface. These so-called "hot spots" were found to be in some cases nearly 50°K warmer than their respective immediate environs, but it should be remembered that the temperature of the eclipsed lunar surface is about 140°K so the hot spots were still extremely cool by terrestrial standards.

Nearly 85% of the thermal anomalies were associated with rayed craters, or those that exhibited bright rims or interiors at full Moon. It was found that the Mare Tranquillitatis contained a concentration of hot spots, and over the entire visible disc more than 400 have been found so far. While no definitive conclusions are yet available it is thought that these spots indicate the positions of areas where the insulating layers of the lunar crust are thinner and where the heat from the lunar interior may find easier egress. This work is still progressing and illustrates the continuing need for ground-based observations of the entire lunar disc.

Sytinskaya, in defence of the meteor slag theory, has suggested that the black volcanic slags, consisting of solidified foams, show the best agreement with the lunar thermal properties, and describes how similar solids could be formed by high-velocity meteoritic bombardment accompanied by extremely high localized temperatures capable of converting some of the lunar material, at the zone of impact, into vapour. On the other hand, it is also pointed out that the outer crust of the Moon cannot consist entirely of impacting material from space for, if this were the case, the albedo or reflection properties of the surface would be very similar over the whole lunar globe, and this is plainly not the case. In fact it would add more weight to the meteor slag theory if the lunar surface did possess a more uniform albedo instead of varying between 5 and 18 % as we noted earlier. Neither can we dismiss entirely the question of lunar vulcanism, for would it not seem just as reasonable to suppose, in view of the undeniably non-uniform surface albedoes, that local vulcanism had provided the black slags required to satisfy this theory? This again is a question that only poses others, for, to answer this, we need to know the nature of the lunar crustal rocks and we shall go round in circles if we ask if lunar and terrestrial rocks have similar compositions, for it is upon this presumed similarity that the whole suggestion is based. In the autumn of 1966 there is no direct answer to this problem and, until the necessary instrumentation is landed on the lunar surface, our best line of attack lies in the abundances of the elements in the Earth, supplemented by those found by spectrographic means in the Sun and the stars. The most abundant elements heading our list, and which appear to be the most probable constituents of the lunar rocks, are oxygen, silicon, aluminium, magnesium, calcium, sodium, potassium and nickel; to these can be added small amounts of sulphur and hydrogen. The abundances of oxygen and silicon, however, far outweigh all the others, so, on this basis, we would expect to find that most of the lunar surface rocks could be classified as silicates. To speculate further on the nature of the lunar rocks at this epoch, standing as we do on the threshold of a bright new era of lunar explorations and analysis, would serve little or no purpose. We know far more about their geometrical structure than their chemical content; nevertheless, this state of affairs is not destined to last much longer* and the astronomer, who has been the lunar custodian for so long, is already handing over these tasks to the geologists.

* See note 2, p. 177.

CHAPTER 5

The Lunar Atmosphere

ABOVE the vast terrestrial oceans, and the continental masses that separate them, lies the Earth's atmospheric ocean—that life-giving mixture of nitrogen and oxygen to which every living creature inhabiting our planet owes its existence. The atmosphere not only supplies the essential gases that are used by mammalian respiratory systems, but, in addition, yields a pressure of 16 pounds per square inch at sea-level. Thus, each square inch of the Earth's surface supports this weight of gas, and this ample thickness or density provides very adequate protection from the dangerous showers of meteoritic particles that would otherwise impinge upon the Earth's surface, sometimes with disastrous results. As well as this, solar radiation, particularly ultra-violet and corpuscular radiation, that are lethal to all forms of terrestrial life, would quickly turn our fertile planet into a barren and lifeless wilderness were it not for the properties of the invisible ocean above our heads. In a nutshell, our evolution, our existence, and the whole future of the human race depends on the purity and richness of our atmosphere, and there is good reason to believe that man is destined to disappear from the Earth in the foreseeable future unless he learns to value the air he breathes and takes the vital decision to prevent its further contamination.

Rocket launchings have been so numerous during the last decade that everyone knows something about the hazards that attend the launchings and recoveries of space capsules. When the vehicles contain astronauts all possible and known risks are minimized, and one of these—the atmospheric heating of the capsule— necessitates the use of heat shields that are made of substances similar to fused silica that will withstand high temperatures in excess of 1000°C. Atmospheric heating, a function of the velocity of the rocket, begins soon after "blast-off" when the rocket is accelerating away from the Earth, but by the time the vehicle has reached escape velocity it is so high, and the air is so thin, that heating does not constitute a problem for the men inside. At re-entry the protection of the space vehicle against overheating becomes a subject of vital importance involving accurate orientation so that the craft descends with its heat shield facing into the re-entry path. If this is not done correctly there is a grave risk that the capsule could burn up like a large meteorite in the Earth's atmosphere.

For many years it has been known that the lunar atmosphere is far less dense than the Earth's and certainly there is no possibility of it ever presenting a heating hazard to astronauts bound for the Moon. With a modest astronomical telescope one can verify by direct scrutiny that the lunar atmosphere is tenuous simply by observing the central regions of the disc, and by comparing their clarity with the image quality of the areas close to the edges or limbs. If any appreciable atmosphere were present the light rays from the limb areas would have to pass through a much greater thickness of gas and would suffer greater degradation, leading to a misting and blurring of details that would not be characteristic of those rays emanating from the centre.

The same telescope will also reveal a lunar disc that is ever free of clouds. It is true that there have been many reports of obscurations which indicate that mists and outgassings sometimes occur on the lunar surface, but these are not to be confused with clouds such as are permanent features of our own atmosphere.

As we have noted earlier, the astronomical photometrist must correct his measurements by taking into account the absorptions of radiation in the Earth's atmosphere. This absorption is at a minimum at the zenith of the observatory and it increases as the secant of the zenith distance. Thus the light of a star, occupying a position in the sky 60° from the zenith, has to pass through an atmosphere that absorbs twice as much as the zenith atmosphere.

This is what astronomers describe as two *air masses*. With a zenith distance of 80°, which is equivalent to an altitude of 10° above the horizon, the star-light has to penetrate about six "air masses" so it is easy to see why astronomers prefer to make their observations when celestial objects attain their highest altitudes in the sky.

At zenith distances close to 90° the secant rule no longer applies, and when the Sun is on the horizon there are no less than 38 "air masses" of terrestrial atmosphere between it and the observer. The absorption in a clear atmosphere per "air mass" amounts to about 0·2 stellar magnitudes in visible wavelengths, so the Sun's light is dimmed by 7·6 magnitudes which is equivalent to a 1100-fold loss in light intensity. In point of fact the Sun's light suffers more than the above figures indicate for we have taken no account of the mists, dusts and smoke of the lower atmosphere.

There are two other related phenomena that are of some importance and which we associate chiefly with sunrise and sunset although they can also be observed at the risings and settings of other celestial bodies, principally the Moon and the planet Venus. The first is the reddening of the light: in such a thickness of atmosphere all but the longer wavelengths are scattered. Secondly, there are the distortions of the images and the bending of the light paths due to refraction. In the first instance solar or lunar discs appear to be flattened, and atmospheric refraction accelerates and delays their apparent respective risings and settings. Thus, when the Sun's disc appears to touch the horizon it is, in fact, below the horizon.

An observer standing on the lunar surface would have no difficulty in proving the existence of a terrestrial atmosphere, and astronomers were not slow in attempting to apply the same principles of detection to a lunar atmosphere. Having failed to discover any differences between the clarity of the lunar central and limb areas, they tried to observe the reddening of stars as they set behind the lunar disc. These stellar occultations also permitted them to compare the actual times of disappearance with the computed time of each event so as to establish if starlight was being refracted by a lunar atmosphere. Needless to say, these experiments never revealed a shred of evidence in support of the existence of a lunar atmosphere.

More recently other workers have introduced sensitive methods of detection but always with negative results and the numerical values that have been given are not due to measured effects but are indeed the limiting values of sensitivity of the instruments employed.

Another investigation involved attempts to detect the twilight glow in the Moon's atmosphere. Given a sufficient density of gas molecules, solar light incident on the Moon should be scattered and refracted into the atmosphere above the darkened hemisphere, just as on Earth we experience a prolongation of daylight after sunset. The phenomenon has often been observed during the crescent phases of Venus.

In view of the unquestioned tenuity of the lunar atmosphere it was essential for astronomers to choose for their measurements those parts of the lunar image where the effects of atmospheric scattering were maximized. From previous arguments connected with our brief survey of some of the optical properties of the terrestrial atmosphere it is obvious that the densest "air masses" in the lunar atmosphere, as observed from the Earth, will be in close proximity to the lunar horizon. In the case of the full Moon the horizon is the hard circular line of demarcation separating the peripheral zones of the disc from the surrounding sky. And this is not all, for lunar phase conditions must be chosen correctly so as to enable the astronomer to measure any spreading of twilight from the illuminated hemisphere to the darkened one. It is also essential for him to choose a lunar phase when both dark and light hemispheres are visible—there would be no virtue in searching for the effect at full Moon when the whole disc is uniformly illuminated.

When the problem is considered in detail it is evident that optimum conditions occur at the quarters when exactly one-half of the lunar disc, as seen from Earth, is illuminated by the Sun, and when the terminator is exactly straight across the disc from north to south satisfying a condition that is described by astronomers as *dichotomy.* In principle, twilight scattering ought to be observable anywhere in the darkened hemisphere adjacent to the line of the terminator, but it is best to seek it at the northern and southern extremities of the terminator in the regions of the polar horizons where any twilight effect is amplified by the denser "air masses". It is here where the astronomer might expect to observe and measure the twilight scattering from the bright hemisphere into the darkened regions.

Finally there must be a method of differentiating between the phenomenon for which the observer is searching and the inherent scattering of light that takes place in his instrument as well as in the sky above him. This brings us to the subject of polarization of light that, in the study of the Moon, was first used by F. Arago, a noted French astronomer and one-time Director of the Paris Observatory, as far back as 1811.

It is now very well established that the reflected light of the Moon is strongly polarized, especially at quadrature, that is when the angle between the Sun, Moon and observer is 90° and when the observer will see the quarter phases. At the full, when the light of the Sun, to all intents and purposes, is shining on the Moon from over the shoulder of the observer, polarization is at a minimum. It is also a fact that the darker areas of the Moon have surfaces that polarize the light more strongly than the lighter continental areas—anyone can test this by gazing through a small piece of polaroid attached to the eyepiece of a telescope and by rotating the polaroid.

Carrying the argument still farther it is also known that a lunar atmosphere—like the Earth's—should exhibit polarization, and when V. G. Fessenkov, a Russian astronomer, first used the polarimetric technique in the early 1940's, he used a polaroid filter and gazed at the centre of the disc, trying to estimate the degree of polarization in the dark area close to the quarter terminators. Y. N. Lipski, another Russian, also tried to make similar observations in 1949 with a special photopolarimeter tuned in to green light: his conclusions implied a lunar atmospheric density of about 1/10,000 of the Earth's atmosphere at sea-level.

However, neither used the technique of looking for scattering in the twilight zones around the lunar poles, and when B. Lyot and A. Dollfus first used this method at the high-altitude Pic-du-Midi Observatory in the French Pyrenees, also in 1949, they were able to reduce the estimated figure to less than 10^{-8} of a standard atmosphere.

In 1952 Dollfus again employed photographic techniques in conjunction with a special Savart–Lyot polariscope using, this time, orange light and he concluded that the maximum density of the lunar atmosphere was no greater than 10^{-9} or one thousand-millionth (one American billionth) of the Earth's atmospheric pressure at sea-level.

This, as it turned out, was destined to be the last word on the subject from the optical astronomers. Despite this, the matter was not allowed to gather dust for very long, for, as so often happens in the fields of scientific endeavour, a tool designed for one task sometimes finds application in other fields of study. The science of radio astronomy was born in the 1930's, raced through adolescence during the 1940's with the new electronic devices of World War II, and attained maturity in the 1950's since when it has revealed important and hitherto unsuspected cosmological discoveries. Most of us have no difficulty in picturing the huge parabolic reflectors of the large radio telescopes that collect and focus on the central antennae the incoming radiations from the stars or, as in the case of the G.P.O. Goonhilly Downs satellite tracking station in south-west England, the bleeps of artificial satellites and the television programmes from across the Atlantic Ocean. Once in a while the Moon passes between us and a far-distant natural radio source and it then becomes possible to estimate the density of the lunar atmosphere on the basis that it contains an ionosphere consisting mainly of free electrons. Radio telescopic measurements of the delay caused by refraction in this ionosphere, as well as diffraction phenomena at the edge of the lunar disc, permit estimates to be made of the electron densities from which may be deduced the lunar atmospheric molecular density. Such estimates, made by Elsmore and Whitfield in 1955, reduced Dollfus's result by a factor of 1000 to less than 10^{-12} of a standard atmosphere, and later work by Costain, Elsmore and Whitfield in 1956 reduced this to 10^{-13}. While the techniques were similar, the radio source used on the second occasion was the Crab Nebula in the constellation of Taurus and this expanding complex cloud of gases is all that is left of a supernova explosion that was recorded by Chinese astronomers in A.D. 1054. This source is also one of the most powerful cosmic transmitters that terrestrial equipment can receive, and it is also interesting to note that the lunar atmospheric assessments were made at wavelengths of 3·7 and 7·9 metres—not too far from the lower-frequency television channels.

It is doubtful if this figure of 10^{-13} of a standard atmosphere can be reduced further until suitable instrumentation is soft-landed on the lunar surface. The fact remains, however, that the overall global atmosphere of the Moon is a very fine vacuum indeed, and most certainly it offers no heat hazard to manned space vehicles passing through it. The astronauts, in some ways, would have welcomed the protection of a denser atmosphere to shield them from the impacts of micrometeorites—but this is just another danger these men will have to face.

Obviously there are many outstanding questions that will have to be pigeon-holed until such time as the answers are forthcoming. Nevertheless, there is one important question that can be answered: and this asks, "Why doesn't the Moon possess an atmosphere similar to the Earth's?"

At first sight it seems reasonable to expect the existence of some sort of permanent atmosphere around the Moon, for, after all, in the Earth–Moon system we have two spherical bodies that are comfortably situated as far as solar light and heat are concerned, and they are not wildly different dimensionally. In the Universe it is more usual to find stars and planets that are thousands of times larger or smaller, instead of the modest 4:1 ratio that we find linking the diameters of the Earth and the Moon. Closer investigation, after we have considered the cubed radii (r^3), while calculating the respective volumes of the two bodies shows that the volume ratio shoots up to a value close to 64:1, and, if the respective densities of the two bodies are utilized, the mass ratio, which is really the quantity we are seeking to evaluate, slightly exceeds 81:1. It turns out that the surface gravity of the Moon is only one-sixth of the Earth's and this is a factor that will assist lunar explorers, for, not only will they themselves feel six times lighter, but they will be able to manipulate heavy loads and perform amazing gymnastic feats that would have been impossible for them to do on the Earth.

The smaller mass of the Moon will also facilitate the launching of space modules back to the parent craft orbiting a few miles above the cratered surface. To break the gravitational bonds holding the space-ship on the lunar surface, enough energy has to be expended to accelerate the craft to a velocity exceeding $1\frac{1}{2}$ miles per second, and, if this seems unduly swift, let us remember that to do the same thing from Cape Kennedy requires a velocity five times greater than this—nearly 7 miles per second!

To discuss launchings and astronauts in a chapter devoted to the lunar atmosphere appears to be a digression, but actually the deviation of the text from the main theme is not great, for astronauts and atmospheres share the common bond of gravitation. For example, if an astronaut were to land on an asteroid possessing feeble gravitation it is more than likely that his more strenuous exertions would accelerate his body to a velocity greater than that required for escape and he would float away into space. The same can happen to gaseous molecules; and the chemical constituents of atmospheres of planets and satellites are dominated by their respective masses and temperatures.

Individual molecules of gases that collectively form terrestrial and other types of atmospheres are often visualized as little spheres in constant and random motion that are packed closely enough together as to make collisions between them frequent events. Most of the time a molecule moves at, or close to, the average velocity of those in its immediate neighbourhood, but there are rarer occasions when a molecule can attain a velocity that is greater than average by borrowing energy from its companions.

We can imagine a situation where a molecule travelling in a certain direction has its speed increased by a collision from behind, and, depending on the mass of the molecule and the temperature of the gas, it is possible for a molecule to attain a velocity that exceeds the escape velocity of the planet or satellite to which it is attached. When such an event happens the molecule launches itself into space and is no longer part of the atmosphere of the body in question, but enlists in the vast army of more adventurous molecules that collectively form the interplanetary medium.

Just as in the earlier days of astronautics, when miniaturized satellites were launched because rockets were not powerful enough to place heavier objects into orbit, it is the lighter molecules that more readily acquire sufficient kinetic energy to escape in this way. The lightest gas of all is hydrogen, and it has been computed that a hydrogen atmosphere would escape from the Moon completely in a matter of a few hours, in fact, on the sunlit side where the temperature reaches more than 100°C, approximately one-third of the hydrogen atmosphere would boil or diffuse away into space during a period of 1 hour. Even on Earth gravity is insufficient to prevent the escape of hydrogen.

Life-giving oxygen, being a molecule 16 times heavier than hydrogen, naturally requires more energy for its launching and on the sunlit side it would take $1\frac{1}{2}$ years for one-third of an oxygen atmosphere to dissipate into space. The remainder would take very much longer to escape because the rate of decay of such an atmosphere is not linear but is a natural logarithmic function, and a small quantity of oxygen would remain for millions of years.

Water vapour could exist only as a vapour on the sunlit hemisphere and one-third of its volume would be lost in 60 years. However, in the intense cold of a darkened hemisphere, at about −120°C, water could remain as ice for 100 thousand million years (10^{11} years). At such temperatures, sublimation—the direct change from the solid to the gaseous phase without the intermediate liquid state—would be an exceedingly slow process, but we must not lose sight of the fact, that, excepting a few crater floors in the lunar polar regions, there are no areas that do not receive the warming rays of the Sun during the period of 1 month. The morsel of information that 100 thousand million years is twenty-two times the estimated age of the Moon need not worry us because we do not possess any real knowledge of the thermal history of our natural satellite since its formation, and, if, as seems likely, the Moon survived a high-temperature phase it would also seem logical to expect that its atmosphere, including its water supply, dissipated quickly and completely into space. If the infant Moon did not experience this calorific treatment there may still remain vestiges of a lunar atmosphere composed of heavier gases such as krypton and xenon.

It is not easy for us to imagine an atmosphere as tenuous as the Moon's, which is only 10^{-13} of a terrestrial standard atmosphere. Perhaps we can appreciate this more easily if we make a comparison between the well-known properties of the terrestrial atmosphere and those of the lunar atmosphere. Let us imagine that by some miraculous means we can remove all of the Earth's atmosphere away from our planet with the exception of a 1-inch-square column that extends from sea-level right up to the atmospheric ceiling. This column of air, as we have noted earlier, weighs 16 pounds. Having accomplished this without going too deeply into the technicalities involved, we can now proceed to release this column of air and permit it to expand sideways in all directions until its density is reduced 10^{-13} times to match the estimated density of the lunar atmosphere. The height of the column does not change. We now have 16 pounds of air occupying a very large volume between the land surface and the upper extremity of the atmosphere, and if we measure the area of the land surface, over which this erstwhile 1-inch-square column has expanded, we find that it now covers 2,500 square miles.

So much for the global atmosphere of the Moon. We may now pass on to other aspects of the same subject. Firstly, if an atmosphere exists at all, there are but two sources from which it can have been derived and these may be described as internal or external. In other words, if the Moon failed to collect an atmosphere gravitationally in its journeying through space, any that it now possesses must have filtered up from beneath its surface.

Occasionally more reliable evidence comes to hand, and some interesting photographic observations were made on 26th October, 1956 by a well-known selenographer, D. Alter, who, at this time, had been using the 60-inch reflecting telescope on Mt. Wilson in California to obtain blue–violet and infrared photographs of the Moon. In the case of the walled plain, Alphonsus, that has more recently become the graveyard of Ranger 9, it was found that rilles and other details on the floor were less sharply defined in the blue–violet photographs than in those secured in infrared wavelengths. Had there been an emission of gas from the surface of Alphonsus during the period of these observations, light of the shorter wavelengths would have been scattered more than its counterpart in the infrared window. Such was the interpretation given to this series of photographs, and some sort of gaseous emission inside Alphonsus was held to be responsible.

The Alphonsus observations stimulated interest in other parts of the world and led N. A. Kosyrev of the U.S.S.R. to point the 50-inch telescope of the Crimean Astrophysical Observatory at the Alphonsus area on the morning of 3rd November, 1958. The observations that he made are of particular interest, and were made at a time just before the shadows of the waning Moon were beginning to slide across the floor of the formation. Kosyrev obtained a spectrogram with a photographic exposure of 30 minutes that, in his opinion, indicated an escape of luminescent gases from the central peak of Alphonsus. He noted also that the peak was whiter and brighter than usual during the time of this exposure, and this appearance was followed by a sudden drop in intensity to the normal appearance in the space of a few seconds. On seeing this transition Kosyrev immediately stopped the exposure and commenced a new one of 10-minutes' duration. The second spectrogram revealed this feature under normal conditions and confirmed his visual impressions. Other spectrograms exposed later showed that the central peak of Alphonsus was behaving normally.

Subsequent analysis of these photographic spectra reveals that, superimposed on the normal spectrum, was another, corresponding to the position of the central peak of the formation, that was characterized by a 40% brightening at a wavelength of 4740Å followed by a system of weak bands with a maximum at 4400Å plus some blurring of the Fraunhöfer line at 4384Å. This spectra was identified as that of the carbon molecule (C_2) and this particular series is known as the Swan resonance bands that are also characteristic of the spectra of comet heads. Further spectrographic work by the same investigator on 23rd October, 1959 revealed a curious "reddening" of a mile-wide area close to the central mountain of Alphonsus. The estimated area of this object was later reduced to about 300 metres in order to satisfy thermal requirements and the postulation of an active lava-flow involving temperatures of around 1000°C. At this point in the story it must be noted that this analysis has not satisfied all lunar experts by any means, and, while Kosyrev's observations have been accepted generally, there are those who subscribe to the view that what he actually recorded was an emission of cool gases from the central region of Alphonsus. Either way it appears that there are gaseous emissions from the lunar interior, but it is equally certain that these events are transitory and sporadic and that the gases concerned are almost immediately dissipated into space.

The release of primordial gases from the interior of the Moon constitutes the main cause of a lunar atmosphere, but recent theories point to other agencies that may play minor roles. For example, it is reasonable—as we have already seen—to assume that some of the upper crustal rocks consist of silicates, and E. J. Öpik has considered the sputtering effect of the "solar wind" protons upon such a surface. The solar wind may here be regarded as a "breeze" of delayed particles that arrives in the Earth–Moon environs as a result of the expansion of the normally invisible outer atmosphere of the Sun, the corona. Since the average flux density is only about 10 particles per cubic centimetre per second at a distance of one astronomical unit (93,000,000 miles), and, since all of these are required to release one atom of the lunar surface, it is evident that any lunar atmosphere formed by this process is negligible. An earlier idea, postulated by T. Gold in 1959, also uses the properties of the solar wind protons to stimulate a constant breeze of hydrogen gas from the sunlit lunar surface, and Öpik has referred to the formation of water molecules as a result of the interaction of solar protons with the upper molecular layers of the crust.

Digging around in the literature unearths all sorts of interesting items of information for, as in most astronomical fields of study, the facts are far outnumbered by the theories, and herein lies the fascination of the subject, for a great deal of effort is expended by astrophysicists in attempting to construct mathematical models based on assumed premises.

CHAPTER 6

Lunar Space Probes

LET us start by reviewing briefly the successes and failures of the first rockets to be directed at the Moon. This takes us back to 2nd January, 1959 when the Russian Lunik 1, weighing 3245 pounds, was launched and missed the Moon by 4660 miles. Lunik 1 is now in orbit and is a minor planet in its own right making a complete revolution about the Sun in 450 days.

Two months later, on 3rd March, 1959, the American Pioneer 4, propelled by a Juno II rocket, was hurled moonwards, but it, too, went into a solar orbit after missing our cosmological companion by 37,000 miles, and it now completes a solar orbit every 398 days.

The first probe to hit the Moon was Lunik 2, launched on 12th September, 1959, and its instrumented payload weighing 858 pounds—approximately the same weight as subsequent Ranger payloads—disintegrated between Autolycus and Archimedes in the Mare Imbrium after a flight of $33\frac{1}{2}$ hours. Shortly afterwards, on 4th October, another Russian probe, Lunik 3, was placed in a very elliptical orbit having a perigee—its closest earth approach— of 25,257 miles and an apogee of 291,439 miles that enabled it to pass behind the Moon where for some 40 minutes it secured the first historical photographs of the averted lunar hemisphere from a distance of 37,000–43,000 miles.

Ranger 1, powered by the mighty Atlas–Agena B rocket, made its début on 23rd August, 1961 and remained in orbit for about 1 week before burning up in the Earth's atmosphere. A similar attempt failed to place an identical vehicle, Ranger 2, into a deep-space orbit on 18th November, 1961, but on 26th January, 1962 a more successful launching achieved deep space, but the

727-pound payload of Ranger 3 missed the Moon by 22,862 miles and became yet another minor planet with a solar revolution of 406 days.

Ranger 4, roaring skywards on 23rd April, 1962, became the first American space probe to hit the Moon in the averted hemisphere after a flight of 64 hours, but an electrical fault in a timing mechanism stopped all of the instrumentation comprising the larger part of its 730-pound payload. Ranger 5 was similarly fated for, following a perfect launching from Cape Canaveral (later Kennedy) on 18th October, 1962, its 755-pound payload of instruments missed the Moon by a modest 450 miles and went into a 366-day orbit around the Sun.

If the American launchings were dogged by bad luck it is also true that the Russians were not doing very much better at the time. On 2nd April, 1963, Lunik 4, weighing 3135 pounds, was directed moonwards but veered from its course sufficiently to miss its target by 5281 miles.

Between the launchings of Rangers 5 and 6 there was an interval of some 20 months, time enough for a reconsideration of the many problems involved and a breathing space in which to complete desirable modifications. The National Aeronautics and Space Administration (NASA) had decided to jettison some of the original experiments and launch four more Rangers—6 to 9 inclusive —with the sole purpose of obtaining close-up photography of the lunar surface. As we shall see, this was a very wise decision.

At this juncture perhaps the reader would like to know something about the rocketry and instrumentation involved in this mighty undertaking. The Atlas–Agena B, as its name implies, is a two-stage launch vehicle comprising an Atlas D first stage possessing a 360,000-pound thrust plus an Agena B second stage with a thrust of 16,000 pounds. The Agena B is programmed for two firings so as to enable the Ranger to be placed initially into a parking orbit around the Earth after which the second firing directs it into a lunar trajectory. The Atlas rocket employs a radio guidance system that can be controlled from the launching site, and the Agena B uses an inertial guidance system. The complete ensemble on the launching pad reaches an impressive total height of 104 feet.

So much for the launch vehicle. The space craft itself consists of a 375-pound conical camera payload unit mounted on what is described affectionately as a hexagonal Ranger "bus". This is enclosed in a polished aluminium casing in which there is a 13-inch aperture at the upper end for the television cameras. The construction of the "bus" is made as lightly as possible by using aluminium and magnesium tubing and struts, and inside it room has to be found for electronic apparatus and the all-important mid-course motor. On the outside a high-gain antenna and two solar power panels are hinged to the base of the craft, and a further so-called omni-directional antenna is mounted on top of the camera payload. With the high-gain antenna deployed and the solar panels hinged outwards, like great arms reaching for the Sun, their total span is 15 feet and the height of the craft is $10\frac{1}{4}$ feet. The total weight is 804 pounds.

The object of the experiment was to project the space-craft to the lunar equatorial regions between the 20° north and south latitudes and within 10–40° of the terminator where the six cameras, switched on some 10 minutes before impact, could make fullest use of the prevailing lighting conditions. At 10° from the terminator the altitude of the Sun is also 10° and this means that a sizeable percentage of the lunar surface will be in black shadow cast by the local relief, and this may seem to waste information. On the other hand, under high Sun angles it is sometimes impossible to find even very large craters because of the absence of shadow to set off the local relief. It is therefore better to sacrifice some information in the shadows if by so doing we gain information in the illuminated regions. As an example, car headlights grazing along a good road surface create for the passing pedestrian an illusion of unevenness that is quite exaggerated. By the same means we can examine the unevenness of the lunar surface using the Sun as our headlamp, and the Ranger missions were designed with this intention in support of the Surveyor and Apollo programmes that will eventually culminate with the manned landing.

In our description of the space-craft payload we ought to mention several important pieces of equipment. Firstly, there is a 3-watt transmitter-receiver to receive commands from the Earth and to transmit data back to the Goldstone tracking station in California. In addition there is an attitude control consisting of nitrogen jets and associated gas bottles together with six Sun sensors, an Earth sensor and three gyroscopes. The function of this equipment is to orientate the space-craft so that the cameras point at the Moon: otherwise they might record only the blackness of space. The mid-course motor is also an essential unit which has been described as a monopropellant hydrazine engine with an 50-pound thrust capability for a maximum time of 98·5 seconds. Its purpose is to make final corrections to the lunar trajectory made previously by the second firing of the Agena B rocket and to ensure that the space-craft does hit the Moon in the right place.

The 4896 solar cells of the outstretched "paddles" plus the built-in silver–zinc batteries yielded a total power of 200 watts. The all-important Ranger television system was divided into two separate channels comprising two F cameras and four P cameras, The circuitry was designed so that each channel was self-contained with a separate power supply, a timer, and a 60-watt transmitter. Each camera used a 1-inch-diameter Vidicon television camera tube and these were exposed sequentially by means of magnetically driven slit-type shutters. The lens of the Fa camera was of 25 millimetres (1 inch) focal length and possessed a focal ratio of 1, and similar lenses were fitted to the P3 and P4 cameras. The Fb camera lens comes into the classification of a telephoto lens with a focal length of 76 millimetres (3 inches) and a focal ratio of 2. Since the size of the image formed by a lens is directly proportional to the focal length of the lens we can see that the Fb images were three times the size of those formed in the focal plane of the Fa camera. The P1 and P2 cameras were fitted with identical lenses, but since each of the P cameras used only a small 2·8-millimetre-square segment of the target area of the Vidicon tube their fields of view were restricted to 2·1° and 6·3° for the P1 and P2 and the P3 and P4 cameras respectively. The largest angular coverage came from the 25° field of the Fa camera while the Fb camera field was restricted to 8·4°.

At this stage let us consider the manner in which the lunar pictures are exposed. The Vidicon television-tube target is composed of a layer of photoconductive material which is scanned and charged up by an electron beam prior to exposure. The focused image formed on the target when the shutter is opened allows the charge to reform according to the varying brightness of the scene. A second electron beam scans the target area, and according to the degree of charge replenishment required, reflected in changes in the beam current, so the scene brightness values are converted into electrical signals that can be amplified and transmitted to the Earth to form once again the basic bricks from which the Ranger photographs can be constructed.

The electron beam in the F cameras scanned the 11-millimetre-square target area in 2·5 seconds using a raster consisting of 1150 lines. The 2·8-millimetre-square P camera targets were scanned by 300-line rasters in 0·2 second. Thus it took twelve times as long to retrieve the F camera signals, but these periods of time should not be confused with the exposure durations of the cameras that had to be very much shorter owing to the fast motion of the space-craft, particularly during the last few seconds before impact. For this reason the shutters of the F cameras were opened for 5 milliseconds (0·005 second) and those of the P cameras for 2 milliseconds (0·002 second).

It is interesting to compare the image-retrieval systems of the Rangers and the earlier Lunik 3. At first sight it could appear that the two projects had much in common, for both were concerned with close-up lunar photography made from space-craft in the neighbourhood of the Moon. However, further consideration reveals that the two assignments are completely different. In the case of Lunik 3 the task was to photograph the averted hemisphere of the Moon and to transmit the signals so that they could be received and reconstructed into pictures on the Earth. Thus the first problem arises from the fact that when the Lunik is behind the Moon no signals from its transmitters can reach the Earth.

This increases the difficulties of using television systems because all of the signals have to be stored on the Lunik until an optical path between the space-craft and the Earth is restored and radio telemetry resumed. The storage of video signals requires magnetic-tape-recording equipment which is both bulky and heavy and poses payload problems and is also a drain on electrical supplies. It is certain that the Russian scientists studied all of these aspects, and many others besides, before deciding to use ordinary 35-millimetre cameras that nevertheless presented them with problems associated with film development and the line-by-line scanning of the negatives. This is the system that was used, and the Lunik instruments translated the film densities into electrical signals that were successfuly relayed back to the Earth.

In the case of the Rangers, photographic methods are ruled out by the fact that the last few photographs would never be developed, let alone scanned, before impact. Also the Rangers' trajectories did not take them behind the lunar globe so there are no transmitting or telemetry problems requiring delays or storage facilities for the television signals. This means that the signals are transmitted instantaneously on two channels from the F and P cameras respectively, and they are received directly and independently on Earth whence they can be recorded on magnetic tape and displayed on the screens of cathode-ray tubes for subsequent photographing on to 35-millimetre film.

There are many more facts relating to the complexities of the Ranger project that the author has omitted, but perhaps enough has been written to show that when a failure takes place it is generally due to some small defect in one of the thousand and one components in the system. So when we hear of failures let us spare sympathetic thoughts for the scientists and technicians who are slowly but surely building these stairways to the stars.

It is now time for us to resume our story with the launching of Ranger 6 that took up a parking orbit after its launching from Cape Kennedy on 30th January, 1964. The term "parking orbit" means that the space-craft is launched into a more or less circular orbit about the Earth, and it can be left there until the scientists below have analysed it and decide when and in what position the craft must be before they press the button that causes the second firing of the Agena B rocket to set the Ranger on course for the Moon. In this instance all went well with the second firing of the Agena B. The solar cell panels were correctly orientated at the Sun, and the antennae systems locked on the Earth, and successful mid-course corrections were made to the trajectory. At the same time attitude adjustments were completed to bring the lunar surface into the fields of the six cameras. It looked as if it was going to be a good shot.

At 19 minutes before impact the F cameras were warmed up and 4 minutes later the P cameras were warmed up as a result of a signal from the Earth—warming up is a necessary operation that must be done before the stable operation of electronic circuitry can be achieved: the same is true of the domestic TV receiver. With only 14 minutes to go to impact the cameras should have started to send back video signals to the Earth. None were received and Ranger 6 destroyed itself upon impact in the western Mare Tranquillitatis after a flight duration of $65\frac{1}{2}$ hours. It has since been accepted that this nearly successful mission was spoiled by a premature switching-on of the television system 2 minutes after the launching that caused electrical arcing and subsequent damage to components.

From now on our story becomes more cheerful, for the launchings of Rangers 7, 8 and 9 were all highly successful as a result of modifications that were made to the command and control circuitry and the television systems. Also the temperature controlling systems were improved and special attention was directed towards the reliability of the electrical components.

Ranger 7 was launched on 28th July, 1964 and 16 minutes and 40 seconds before impacting on the Moon it began to relay back to Earth 4316 high-quality photographs. Some 400 wide-angle (F camera) and 3900 narrow-angle (P camera) photographs were transmitted, and the first of these, taken at a height of 1120 miles above the lunar surface, covered an area of 400 miles square. The last frame, taken from a height of 1000 feet, revealed an area of

60 × 100 feet—about the size of a tennis court—in which details down to 1½ feet could be resolved. The impact of Ranger 7 occurred at 13 hours 25 minutes 49 seconds on 31st July following a flight of 243,665 miles completed in 68 hours and 35·55 minutes. The point where the 5850-mile-per-hour impact took place was in the Guericke area of the Mare Nubium. Later, at the International Astronomical Union Meeting in Hamburg in 1964, it was pointed out that this area was not really a part of the Mare Nubium and, following a suggestion of Dr. G. P. Kuiper that the region should be named the Mare Cognitum, the assembly finally adopted this name—the Known Sea.

The launchings of Rangers 8 and 9 were essentially similar to that of Ranger 7. The launching dates were 17th February and 21st March, 1965, respectively, and Ranger 8 impacted into the Mare Tranquillitatis—not far away from the debris of Ranger 6—at 10 hours 07 minutes 21 seconds on 20th February. Ranger 9 was aimed at the centre of Alphonsus where it fell only three miles off target at 14 hours 08 minutes 20 seconds on 24th March, 1965. This was very accurate indeed.

Perhaps the major difference between the two flights was the manner in which each craft "homed" in on its target. In the case of Ranger 8 the final plunge was made obliquely (49° from the vertical) which, when one studies the photography, gives an impression of a dive across a large area of the lunar surface. In fact 900,000 square miles were recorded on 7137 photographs and, owing to the oblique approach, the impact area was not recorded at all, neither was the resolution of the photography so good because of blurring—the best resolution obtained from this series of photographs was 5 feet which means that craterlets 5 feet across could be seen distinctly. Altogether different was the lunar approach of Ranger 9, and the impact area could be seen on photographs secured several minutes before impact from a height of about 300 miles, and, thereafter, it was possible to follow the descent in successive frames until the last, taken from a height of 2000 feet, showed the tiny craterlet upon whose rim the spacecraft crashed to destruction. Ranger 9 returned 5814 pictures of high quality, covering 600,000 square miles near the centre of the Moon's visible hemisphere, and the best frames resolved features as small as 15 inches in diameter. Truly this was a remarkable achievement and one that will not be easy to dislodge from its niche in the annals of astronautics.

So ended the successful Ranger Programme that had been conceived as far back as 1959. Before we proceed to the next chapter to discuss the findings of the Rangers we must also consider some of the other lunar probes that were launched at the Moon by the Americans and Russians, and perhaps we can weave their discoveries into the same fabric.

The Russian Luniks 5 and 6 took wing very soon after the last of the Rangers. These were designed to soft-land on the lunar surface and to relay pictures of the surface back to Earth. Lunik 5, weighing 3254 pounds, soared moonwards of 9th May, 1965 and made a hard impact on the Moon—no meaningful signals were relayed back before impact. Lunik 6, weighing 3179 pounds, left in hot pursuit on 8th June, 1965—just 1 month later—and this probe went into a heliocentric orbit after it had missed the Moon by 100,000 miles: thus the solar system has acquired another unnatural planet. Zond 3, another type of Russian space probe, left its pad on 20th July, 1965, and, after taking up a parking orbit around the Earth, it was injected into what is called a "deep-space trajectory" and after 33 hours the probe passed by the Moon. Zond 3 took twenty-five photographs at distances of 5730 – 7190 miles over a period of 68 minutes, but these were not relayed back to Earth until 9 days later when the space probe was 1,400,000 miles from home. These transmissions were accomplished by means of a narrow-beam antenna locked on the Earth and the initial transmission took 34 minutes per photograph. In this connection it is worth noting that these were photographs that had to be processed on board the craft in a similar manner to those of Lunik 3. The camera used for this task was fitted with a 100-millimetre focal length lens working at a focal ratio of 8. For the benefit of the non-photographic reader the focal ratio of a lens is merely the focal distance divided by the aperture; thus we can deduce that the aperture of the Zond 3 lens was a modest 12·5 millimetres ($\frac{1}{2}$ inch). Exposures of 1/100 and 1/300 second were made on 25-millimetre film—25 millimetres, by the way, is a most unusual width of film. Each picture was transmitted by cutting each into a raster comprising 1100 lines which gives about twice the resolution of the standard European 625-line television raster. Zond 3's photography covered some 2 million square miles of the lunar surface including much of the averted hemisphere and most of what had not been observed by the Lunik 3 cameras in 1959. It is known that the launch-vehicle was a multi-stage rocket but the weight and description of the space-craft has never been disclosed, and it must be assumed, since it carried other experimental equipment to measure terrestrial and interplanetary magnetic fields, solar wind, low-frequency galactic radio emissions, micrometeoroids, cosmic rays, lunar infrared and ultra-violet spectra, that it must have been both large and weighty. Zond 3, like some of its predecessors, has now become a planet orbiting the Sun.

Lunik 7 was launched by the Russians on 4th October, 1965 and it was intended that this space probe should soft-land its 3318-pound payload on to the lunar surface, but, after a flight time of 86·1 hours, the retro-rockets fired too early and the craft crashed on to the lunar surface. If the retro-rockets fire too early this can be just as disastrous to the space probe as if they do not fire at all—either way the craft will be destroyed upon impact.

On 3rd December, 1965 the fourth Russian attempt to send a soft-landing probe to the Moon resulted in the launching of Lunik 8. Probably 1965 will be remembered by the Russian space scientists as being a particularly frustrating year, for on this occasion the retro-rockets fired too late and before they had time to slow the craft down it had ploughed its grave in the lunar soil. Thus ended 1965 on a somewhat dismal note.

The year 1966, as well as being the 900th anniversary of the Battle of Hastings and the 300th of the Great Fire of London, saw the first successful soft-landings of space probes on to the surface of the Moon. It would therefore be no overstatement to say that a new era of planetary exploration was ushered in by the new year of 1966. In the case of the Moon the Russians were off the mark first, when Lunik 9 soared upwards on 31st January, 1966. Three and a half days afterwards came the triumphant announcement that Lunik 9 had soft-landed in the Oceanus Procellarum close to the large craters, Reiner and Marius. Retro-rockets had fired at 18 hours 44 minutes G.M.T. and the landing had taken place $1\frac{1}{2}$ minutes afterwards, and after a short silence the spacecraft had started to transmit a series of close-up television pictures of its immediate neighbourhood that had been received, not only by the Russian scientists, but also by British radio astronomers using the 250-foot-diameter radio telescope at Jodrell Bank in Cheshire.

Later it was revealed that the television camera and associated equipment had not been soft-landed directly, but had been contained in a 200-pound shock-resistant ball that had been ejected from Lunik 9 several hundred feet above the lunar surface. This, in fact, was not the sort of soft-landing that a man could survive, nevertheless it served the purpose for which it was intended and a most remarkable set of television pictures were received—the first ever close-ups of the mysterious surface of the Moon.

The news of the Russian success was quickly disseminated by the Press, and, for a day or two afterwards, "lunar" headlines and close-up pictures of the lunar crust and columns of details and speculations pushed world affairs off the front pages of the newspapers. As ever, the well-worn cliché was repeated that, "This event now puts the Russians ahead in the race for the Moon".

Four months were to elapse before a reappraisal of the situation produced the following headline in an English newspaper, "Soft landing on the Moon puts U.S. ahead in Space". This volte-face was triggered off by the news of the first American soft-landing made by Surveyor 1 which was launched at 14 hours 41 minutes G.M.T. —that is the same as Universal Time (U.T.)— on 30th May, 1966. The landing took place at 06 hours 17 minutes 14 seconds G.M.T. on 2nd June in a Procellarian "ghost ring" named after the first Astronomer Royal, John Flamsteed (1646–

1719). The selenographic co-ordinates of the resting place of Surveyor 1 have been given as longitude $-43\cdot4°$, latitude $-2\cdot4°$ and its position may be found in quadrant 3 of the chart at the end of this volume.

The descent of the Surveyor 1 on to the lunar surface provides a fascinating story which is worth recounting in these pages because it really is the first soft-landing about which there is no shortage of technical information. Besides, most people—and the author was no exception—do not have the remotest idea of the complexities involved in making a success of a feat of this magnitude.

As far as Moon-shots are concerned it has become more or less standard practice to place the probe into a parking orbit with a rocket attached to it so that a second firing can be made to inject the probe into a deep-space trajectory. In the case of the Rangers the launch vehicle was the Atlas–Agena B and it is interesting to note that the Surveyors used the Atlas to get them off the launching pads at Cape Kennedy. The second stage, however, was called the Centaur which can probably be best described as a more powerful relation of the Agena B. After the Centaur had completed its second burning to place the Surveyor on its correct path to the Moon it was jettisoned, and the probe continued its Ranger-like flight through space. During this part of the journey the craft was oriented until special sensors locked on the Sun and the bright southern hemisphere star, Canopus. This star is often used for such purposes because it is the second brightest in the whole sky—as seen from the solar system—and also because it is nearly 53° away from the equatorial regions and can never be found in the same part of the sky as the Sun, Moon and planets. Sirius, the brightest star, is only $16\frac{1}{2}°$ south of the equator, so its use could cause some confusion.

As the Surveyor proceeded towards the Moon a signal from Earth was received and corrections were made to the orientation and three small rockets were fired to adjust the course. All systems were going as planned.

For the landing on an airless world, where parachutes are as worthless as a punctured inflatable raft is to a shipwrecked mariner, braking has to be achieved by rocket motors, and this necessitates an accurate knowledge of the attitude or orientation of the craft in space. If by some accident, the craft is approaching its target head first—that is, the same attitude in which it departs from its launching pad—the firing of the retro-rockets will have a cumulative effect, and, instead of slowing down as intended, the craft will accelerate with disastrous results. The task confronting the space engineer is one of turning the space-craft so that it will descend stern first, thus giving it an attitude that will permit the thrust of the retro-rockets to cancel out the initial velocity of the flight through space. For this purpose the Surveyor carried nitrogen gas jets, and, for the main task of a soft landing, a solid-fuel retro-motor and three liquid fuel vernier rockets were also put on board. For those readers who have an interest in chemistry, each vernier engine possessed a pair of tanks containing fuel and oxidizer, respectively, and the contents of these were forced into the engine by deflating the tanks with helium. Spontaneous ignition took place when the fuel—monomethyl-hydrazine monohydrate—was mixed with the oxidizer—nitrogen tetroxide and nitric oxide. The thrust of these engines was made variable over the range 30–104 pounds.

At the height of 1000 miles above the Moon the Surveyor was turned to line up with the flight path so as to facilitate the "feet-first" descent. The turning was assisted by the use of gyroscopes, and, when the craft had reached the 200-mile altitude, a command was given and the altitude-marking radar was switched on, and this device controlled all subsequent manoeuvres automatically. Surveyor continued its descent towards the Moon until the solid-fuel retro-motor was ignited at a height of 60 miles—3 minutes to touchdown. The braking effect of the retro-motor was so fantastic that numbers alone do not provide any sort of yard-stick by which its performance can be gauged. Short of experiencing this violent retardation and living to tell the tale afterwards, how can anyone appreciate the effect of slowing down from 6000 miles to a mere 250 miles per hour in the space of 40 seconds?

After the 1377-pound retro-motor had done its job it was jettisoned at a height of 33,000 feet above the lunar surface and the liquid-fuel rockets continued the task of the soft landing. At 12,000 feet the speed was still about the same—400 feet per second—but this was reduced to 250 feet per second at an altitude of 8000 feet after which the braking effect of the liquid-fuel vernier motors became more effective. It has been reported that the Surveyor virtually stopped above the lunar surface at a height of 13 feet whence the motors were cut to prevent dust disturbances on the crust below, and the craft fell at a speed of 10 feet per second and upon landing rebounded $2\frac{1}{2}$ inches. Had there been a human passenger aboard he would have experienced a mild shaking that would have done him no bodily harm, especially since the three legs of the Surveyor were fitted with aircraft-type shock absorbers tipped with crushable pads of honeycomb aluminium.

Standing in the ghost ring Flamsteed, with its three feet straddling a circle 14 feet in diameter, the horizon of the 10-foot-high Surveyor 1 was about 1 mile away. All extraneous materials had been jettisoned, and it is worth noting that at the launching the craft had weighed 2,194 pounds, but the discarded retro-motor plus used propellants and attitude-control gases had accounted for more than two-thirds of this weight. The payload that had finally found the lunar surface weighed a modest 620 pounds.

From the point of view of construction, and as would be expected, great use had been made of the lighter metals, especially aluminium tubing. Thus there was a main space frame and, hinged to this, folding booms for two omnidirectional antennae. Also, after landing, a vertical mast was extended supporting a planar antenna and a solar panel: these were designed so that they could be turned in any direction to face the Earth and Sun respectively. The solar panel provided about 60 watts of electricity for running the transmitters and associated equipment, and during the long lunar night power came from silver–zinc batteries.

We can discount completely any notion that suggests that the successful soft-landing of Surveyor 1 was just a lucky event. It is true that a certain modicum of luck is necessary at the launching —the vagaries of terrestrial weather can, and often do, delay launchings; but after the space vehicle has dragged itself above the atmosphere there are no more disturbing influences in space to make it deviate from its intended course. Careful planning, the thorough investigation of every problem no matter how trivial, experiments, trials—all these were done and redone until near-perfection was achieved. The influence of Lady Luck plays a very minor role in such projects.

The television camera on Surveyor 1 was mounted in a vertical position so that its lens pointed upwards into a mirror that was capable of rotation through an angle of 360° in azimuth. This mirror also tilted up and down and the two movements were combined so as to permit the camera to view the complete environment of the space-craft. Thus it scanned the surface below, including its own feet, and it lifted its lens to the hills—the low ridgy walls of Flamsteed were identified from existing lunar charts —and up into the black daytime lunar skies where it recorded some of the brighter stars. And all this was made possible without having to move the camera at all—it was all done by mirrors.

For those who are interested in cameras, the television camera lens possessed a flexibility of focus from 4 feet to infinity—how else could it record its own feet as well as the far-distant stars? As has become standard practice in commercial film cameras the TV lens also included an iris diaphragm that adapted its aperture to the prevailing lunar light level as a result of a signal from a photoelectric cell. Provision was also made for time exposures— a facility of some importance during the lunar night—and additional equipment took the form of a filter wheel containing coloured and polarizing filters. With the former it would be feasible to assess the colour of the lunar surface and with the latter obtain close-up polarimetry of the surface layer.

The first pictures to be received on 2nd June, 1966 via the 210-foot paraboloidal antenna at Goldstone in California were 200-line raster low-resolution pictures obtained from battery-operated equipment. On this system one frame could be transmitted to Earth every 61·8 seconds. This is seventeen times slower than the transmission of the high-resolution frames, that, following the erection of the retractable mast, were received at a rate of one frame per 3·6 seconds.

These, then, are a few of the bald facts about the Surveyor project: obviously there is much that could be said about it, for seven missions are planned. As well as television photography many other studies are included that will yield a wealth of information about the Moon. We could discuss the touchdown dynamics experiments employing strain gauges, accelerometers and rate gyroscopes to determine the achieved bearing strength of the lunar surface. Other experiments involve the use of pantograph mechanisms to dig trenches across the crust in full view of the TV cameras.* Again there are micrometeorite detectors, alpha backscattering equipment to analyse the composition of the lunar material and seismometers to establish the frequency of "Moonquakes".

We have nearly reached the end of this chapter dealing with the nature of lunar probes past and present, and I hope that the reader will bear with me while I discuss briefly the American Lunar Orbiter. Already, as I write (September 1966), there are two Russian Orbiters, Luniks 10 and 11, revolving round the Moon and there is also the first American Lunar Orbiter launched on 10th August, 1966, just a few days in advance of Lunik 11.

In putting up the lunar orbiters we must assume that both nations have similar aims in view, for there are only a few tasks that such craft can accomplish. The main one undoubtedly is the acquisition of high-resolution topographical data to assist in the choice of suitable sites for the manned landings. This involves the strip-by-strip coverage of certain chosen areas, the work being performed in the same way as a high-flying, camera-carrying aircraft photographs the Earth. These data brought back to Earth provide the chart-makers with valuable close-up photography of far superior quality than any obtainable through terrestrial telescopes. In the case of the American Lunar Orbiter the photographic programme was designed to last from 15 to 30 days. This, by the way, is a photographic and not a television technique and therein lies the main problem, for there are severe limitations on the

* See note 3, p. 177.

amounts of film that can be carried and processed and, afterwards, scanned electronically prior to the transmissions back to Earth. In addition to the topographic programme, other studies include gravitational phenomena, measurements of micrometeoritic fluxes and radiation data acquisition. These programmes are designed to last much longer than the photographic work, in fact they can be extended up to about 1 year. Since all of these studies are in support of the American Apollo Programme to place two men on the Moon by 1969 it is absolutely essential to investigate the effects of the lunar mass on bodies orbiting close to the surface. Likewise, as has been pointed out earlier, there may yet be considerable hazards from micrometeorites and solar radiations.

One of the most important pieces of equipment that the inquisitive Orbiter carries is the 150-pound camera system. In effect there are two cameras, one with a 24-inch focal length $f/5\cdot6$ lens and another with a 80-millimetre focal length $f/5\cdot6$ lens. At perilune, when the Orbiter is only 29 miles above the ground, the 24-inch lens provides 1-metre resolution of a strip of ground approximately $10\frac{1}{2}$ miles long by $2\frac{1}{2}$ miles wide. The 3-inch lens simultaneously affords 8-metre resolution over an area of 350 square miles. The total amount of 70-millimetre film carried on the craft permits high-resolution photography over 3000 square miles and medium-resolution images over 14,000 square miles—the latter area, by the way, is just one-thousandth of the total lunar surface. When the exposures have been completed the film has to be developed and fixed like any other film, and the Eastman Kodak Company have built the equipment for doing this. In the absence of human astronauts it has, of necessity, to be first and foremost a fully automated machine. Secondly, the tasks of developing and fixing are combined and the adjective that would more aptly describe the monochemical process used for this phase of operations would be "damp" instead of the traditional "wet".

Following the chemical processing of the lunar negatives they pass through an electronic scanning system comprising, on the one hand, a high-intensity electron beam and, on the other, a photoelectric device that registers the changes in intensity of the beam as the film passes between. In this way each individual film density is converted into an electrical signal that can be transmitted to Earth. At this stage we encounter one of the difficulties that was experienced with Lunik 3, namely that each time the Orbiter passes behind the Moon radio signals are unable to be transmitted back to Earth. To combat this problem the designers of Orbiter arranged that one frame of high-resolution together with one frame of medium-resolution photography should be telemetred only during the 67-minute period when the craft is visible in the radio sense. It has been said that to transmit the total photographic data on board requires 14 days to complete at 43 minutes per pair of frames.

If the Orbiter were an enormous craft with no film-storage or handling problems it is evident that it could continue to take high-resolution photographs until the whole 14,000,000 square miles of the Moon's surface had been recorded on film.* While fuels and payloads follow the restrictive patterns of present-day achievements an undertaking such as this will not be feasible in the foreseeable future, and by then perhaps it may be more practicable to think in terms of direct retrieval of the film. Otherwise there will be the gargantuan task of having to devise an apparatus to transmit each item of information to terrestrial laboratories. Each picture is composed of many thousands of pieces, or "bits", that have to be reassembled in the correct order. The higher the resolution of the picture the more bits there are, and it may be something of a shock to learn that an Orbiter carries in its $5\frac{1}{2}$-foot-high construction sufficient film storage to provide approximately 10^{12} bits of information, and this represents only a tiny fraction of the total lunar requirement. That is why Orbiter photography is restricted to lunar equatorial areas within longitudes $42°$ to $-56°$ for this is where a search is going on for a suitable landing site for the Apollo Project.

* See note 4, p. 177.

CHAPTER 7

The New Moon

IN CHAPTER 4 we reviewed some of the theories relating to the nature of the lunar surface as it appeared to ground-based astronomers and physicists less than half a decade ago. This last chapter seeks to weave into this background tapestry the discoveries made by the space probes that we have just finished discussing. How have our conceptions of the Moon changed? What does our new Moon look like at close quarters? How close to the truth were the older pre-astronautical theories? All of these are pertinent questions, and although we have scarcely set foot along the road of lunar exploration we can, at least, attempt to answer some of them. This seems to be a suitable juncture to point out to the reader that much of what has been discovered by the Moon-probes has merely posed new questions.

Let us refresh our memories with a few facts and figures pertaining to the resolution of ground-based telescopes because, before we can learn anything new about the Moon's surface, we must set a division between the attainable and the unattainable from terrestrial observatories. The limitations of all ground-based telescopes are set by the Earth's atmosphere as we have already noted, that is why we must despatch our celestial messengers above it to sample the unattenuated and undistorted radiations of extra-terrestrial space.

Discounting the disturbing effects of the atmosphere, the resolution of a telescope is a function of its clear aperture. We have all heard of and seen photographs of some of the world's largest astronomical telescopes in the western United States, and we might well enquire as to their performances, especially in connec-

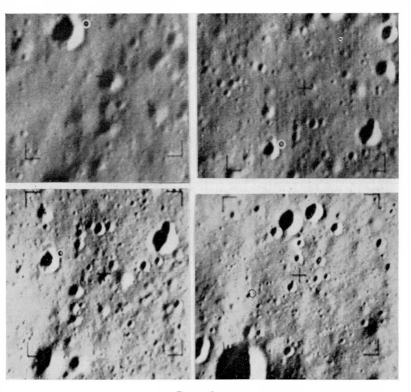

PLATE 2.

These are the four last P frames of Ranger 9 before its impact in Alphonsus on 24th March, 1965 at 14 hours 08 minutes 19·75 seconds U.T. (G.M.T.). The impact area is marked by a circle on each frame. The photographs are in the following sequence: P2 (bottom left) height above ground 7500 feet, 0·888 seconds to impact; P4 (upper left) height 5460 feet, 0·688 seconds to impact: P1 (lower right) 3550 feet and 0·448 seconds. Lastly P3 (upper right) 1960 feet and 0·248 seconds to impact.

PLATE 3.

This is a Ranger 9 FA camera photograph taken at a height
of 236 miles and 2·8 minutes to impact on 24th March, 1965
at 14 hours 05 minutes 38·3 seconds U.T. (G.M.T.). The heavily
cratered floor of Alphonsus is shown left of centre, while to the
lower right can be seen part of the floor of Mare Nubium. Area for
area crater counts show that the Nubium crater population is less
than that of the floor of Alphonsus. The large crater upper right is
Alpetragius.

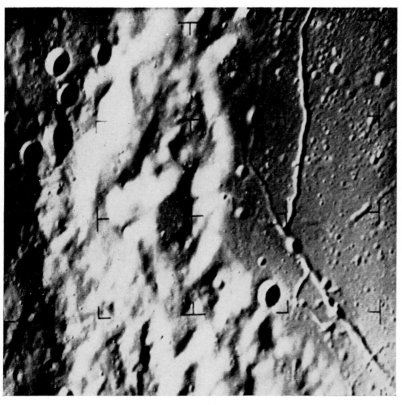

PLATE 4.

This Ranger 9 FB camera photograph taken from a height of 167 miles and 1·9 minutes to impact shows clearly one of the dark haloed craters between the most prominent rille and the bright wall in the upper right area of the picture. Note the few small craters within the halo and also the filling of the rilles either side of the main crater in the halo. Extreme right is a good example of one of the "gouge-type" valleys.

PLATE 5.

This is a Ranger 9 FA camera photograph showing the floor of Alphonsus from a height of 55 miles and 36·7 seconds to impact. Note the whiteness and comparative smoothness of the 3500-foot central peak and the multitudes of craters of all sizes that bespatter the floor.

tion with lunar visual and photographic observations. Given perfect optics and perfect observing conditions, the largest telescope in the world, the 200-inch-diameter reflecting telescope of Mount Palomar in California would resolve a lunar crater about 100 yards across, and a linear feature, such as a narrow rille or fault, could be glimpsed if it were about 10 yards wide. This would be its visual performance under impossibly good atmospheric conditions and also what a 200-inch telescope could resolve if it were in orbit above the atmosphere. If this last statement seems utterly fantastic to the reader he might be interested to learn that the Boeing Company already have advanced plans to launch a Manned Orbiting Telescope of about 120-inches diameter—those readers who are interested should look up Z. Kopal's "Telescopes in Space" in *Science Journal*, April 1966.

In reality the performance of such a telescope falls far short of the figures given above, and researches conducted at Manchester University, under the direction of Z. Kopal, and with the 43-inch reflecting telescope at the Pic-du-Midi Observatory, indicate that in the main the resolution of any large telescope seldom exceeds that of the 43-inch that has produced some of the world's finest lunar photography. In other words, there are not many places on the Earth where the atmosphere is stable enough to permit even a large-aperture telescope to function any better than one of 43 inches diameter. From this we may surmise that we shall not be greatly in error if we assume that craters of about 300 yards diameter and rilles and faults of about 25 yards in width represent the best lunar resolution attainable visually from the Earth. Photographically we are fortunate if we can resolve features as small as this, so, up to the beginning of the present astronautical era, all of our direct "optical" knowledge of the lunar surface was based upon what we could see of macrosurface features down to a few hundred yards across.

How much better then were the resolving powers of the Ranger camera lenses just before their fragments were strewn over the lunar surface by the abruptness of their arrival? The answer is quickly forthcoming: the Ranger photographic resolution was nearly 1000 times better than any so far obtained from ground-based telescopes. To be more precise, the best resolution was achieved by Rangers 7 and 9, whose cameras both showed details down to $\frac{1}{2}$ metre on the lunar crust. Ranger 8 descended much more obliquely, as we noted in the last chapter, and for this reason the close-up pictures show some blurring that limited the best resolution to about $1\frac{1}{2}$ metres. This, however, does not tell the whole story. Photographic resolution is not a simple conception and there are many other factors that influence it, but most of these have no place in a book dedicated to the Moon. There is a lunar effect that does greatly influence resolving power and this is the angle at which the solar rays strike the lunar ground and light it up, and it is a well-known phenomenon—not only on the Moon but anywhere else too—that low relief is amplified by low angles of illumination. This is very easy to demonstrate with a movable table-lamp and a table-cloth: ridges and valleys in the cloth that are quite invisible under high angles of illumination appear very clearly under grazing angles. In similar context the resolution of the Ranger photography became dependent on the prevailing angles of illumination above the points of impact. For example, Ranger 7's photography is not so dramatic as that of Ranger 8, and Ranger 9's photographs are easily the most satisfying. The solar altitude angles at the points of impact were 23°·2, 14°·7 and 10°·4 respectively—yes, indeed, the angle of illumination plays an important part (see Plate 2).

We may now pose the question and ask what new lunar features have been found by the Rangers that lie beyond the resolving threshold of ground-based telescopes. The answer is a little surprising for it seems, at whatever scale one chooses, that the general pattern of the lunar ground presents a familiar sameness. Both high- and low-altitude frames show roughly the same pattern composed of a few large craters, larger numbers of smaller ones, and multitudes of miniature craters and craterlets. Even in those Ranger photographs secured only a few moments to impact, we still see the same general variations on the theme, the spattering of larger craters and multitudes of smaller ones, smooth hills and mountains, rilles and valleys, wrinkle ridges and groove-like depressions that look as if they have been gouged across the lunar surface by a malevolent giant. All of these characteristics can be discerned in ever-decreasing sizes right down to the ½-metre limitations imposed by the Ranger optics.

One of the last Ranger 8 B-camera photographs, taken at an altitude of 5 miles and as many seconds to impact, shows an unusual circular depression that presents an appearance more like that of a mouth of a trumpet. This is another way of saying that if one were able to descend into this 200-yard-diameter depression the slopes would increase toward the centre, making the descent more difficult, and this is contrary to what we would expect because most lunar craters possess shapes like tea-saucers and are therefore more steep in the peripheral regions than in the centres. In this context we, are, of course, omitting the effects of central peaks that would not make walking any easier.

Many of these dimple depressions have been discovered in the close-up Ranger photographs and here again, while no final explanation is yet available, there is a tendency to regard these objects as collapse features. In our ignorance let us suppose that there exist, just below the lunar surface, large spherical cavities that once held magma that afterwards found an outlet and drained away. Subsequent cooling and contraction might easily result in the fracturing of the roof of such a cavity that would collapse to form the dimple-type formation. That is one way: another way of producing such a feature would be by the process of drainage in which the more fluid surface lavas could drain back into the subsurface cavities through what might be described as sink-holes similar to terrestrial sinks found in the limestone areas. A region containing large numbers of sink-holes is said to display karst topography, a name that it gets from a plateau region of northeastern Italy and Yugoslavia, and this could, in fact, be descriptive of these lunar areas as long as we do not associate limestone with the Moon.

Lunar Dust

Fortunately for us the optics of the Lunik 9 and the Surveyor 1 carried on from approximately where the Ranger photography fizzled out, and the first surprise—not to say shock for some scientists—came as a result of the discovery of the absence of lunar and cosmic dust on the surface. Possibly this statement requires further explanation. Firstly, it is unlikely that individual grains of dust would show up in the televised pictures for, earlier in this book when we were discussing lunar dust, we came across estimated dimensions of dust grains in the range 1 to 100 microns. To convey the TV images of particles of these sizes to the Earth would require the use of microscope lenses capable of many linear magnifications so that an image of an individual grain would be many times larger than the size of the electronic scanning spot. Neither craft was equipped with TV microscope systems and 1 millimetre represents a reasonable estimate of the best resolution that was obtained. No, the announced absence of dust can be meaningful only in the collective sense, that is, we have to envisage dust deposits that are sufficiently deep to cover crustal rocks in a manner something like fine sand covers some of our sea-shores. And the first pictures from Lunik 9 showed absolutely nothing to substantiate this idea. Imagine if you can a jagged surface of rock having the appearance of irregularly torn sponge. This is is the micro-character of a surface that contains small craterlets and depressions in addition to rocky edifices of a few inches to several feet in height. Nothing is smooth or gentle in this wilderness that stretches to an undulating horizon about a mile away. The harsh lighting of the Sun, unsoftened by the blue scattering of a daylight sky, emphasizes the relief: no boulder, stone, crevice or crater is without its dense black shadow. This is the skeleton—the bare grey husk of a lifeless world that, by comparison, would make the Sahara Desert seem like the promised land.

As to the existence or absence of dust, no definite assertions can be made at present, for both of the soft-landers touched down in the Oceanus Procellarum far away from any bright ray systems.

If ray systems are composed of ejecta deployed radially around craters such as Copernicus and Tycho (to satisfy this idea we must assume that mighty explosions of internal or external origin excavated these vast arenas in the first place) then it would be logical to expect that dust exists in deep layers in these areas unless the dust has found some way of cementing itself together to form solid rock. It is to be hoped that one of the Surveyors may soft-land in a bright ray region and produce the necessary data to put an end to these speculations. Such a landing would also tell us if the large craters were made by explosive forces.

An alternative point of view—not a new one by any means since the author remembers Z. Kopal, Professor of Astronomy at Manchester, discussing this topic at least eight years ago—outlines the possibility of comets hitting the Moon to cause the formation of the craters. A comet, contrary to popular belief, is not a massive object, but it is nevertheless true that when a comet is close to the Sun it can grow a luminous tail that may be millions of miles in length. While a comet tail is not much denser than surrounding space, the so-called head is generally supposed to consist of rocky fragments, dusts, ices and gases, and it is the warmth and radiation pressure of the Sun that releases material in the head and pushes it away in the antisolar direction to form the tail. G. P. Kuiper and E. A. Whitaker have suggested that Tycho- and Copernicus-type craters may have been formed by the heads of comets striking the Moon; and the secondary craters and rays by comet fragments outside the epicentre. If we can imagine the circular waves that spread out from the point where a pebble is dropped in a pond, we can also understand how an expanding column of gas can spread out, from the point of impact of a comet on the Moon, to cause a wind that would help to deploy the rays radially away from the parent crater. Computations along these lines have shown that the masses of comets are sufficient for the purpose, and the wind is more easily obtainable from the volatile comet gases than from the vaporized silicates of the lunar surface rocks. Even if this turns out to be the true explanation we might still expect to find dust as a by-product in the rays. Whether it will be found in loose form or compacted or welded into rock is another thing—we have a long way to go before the final chapter can be written on the subject of lunar dust.

Lunar Vulcanism

If we no longer have the right to envisage gigantic dust-bowls forming the lunar maria, what can we reinstate in their place? Let us face up to the problem and consider the different agencies that may yet be, or at least have been, at work moulding the lunar crust into the shapes and surfaces we see at the present time. There are not many of them to choose from. Discounting the large-scale migration of dust from the highlands to the lowlands in the manner suggested by Gold, we can think in terms of water as an agency for smoothing the maria but only if the Moon were a lot more massive than it is today. Unprotected water could not remain for very long on the lunar surface but would rapidly boil off into space—even more problematical would be to get it there in vast quantities in the first place. The planet Mars, which is about ten times as massive as the Moon, has little enough water, so, if this body has not been massive enough to retain its oceans, we must surely abandon any notions of there ever having been "wet" seas and oceans on the Moon.

This really narrows the field: if dust and water are excluded we are left with only one plausible solution—vulcanism. This does not mean that we have to invoke Nasmyth's late-nineteenth-century volcanic fountains that ejected neat and symmetrical umbrellas of lava and cinders to build up the ramparts around the central cones of lunar craters. Neither do we necessarily require volcanoes as we find them on the Earth's surface. The term "vulcanism" is used here in its broadest meaning—the endogenic or internal heating of the subsurface rocks to produce magma that emerges through fractures in the surface to make lava flows. And if the surface is weak and loosely aggregated as is suggested by the findings of the radio astronomers there is less reason to suppose that enormous forces and pressures are required to complete this process. Let us suppose that the surfaces of the maria are indeed composed of lava flows—the opinions of some of the experts are tending in this direction—then these will be very much older than those found on the Earth and, for this reason, they would not necessarily be recognized as such by anyone familiar with terrestrial and younger basaltic rocks. The lunar scenery, as revealed by Lunik 9 and Surveyor 1, bears a greater resemblance to the loose cindery ejecta of new terrestrial volcanoes like Paricutin in Mexico whose 9000-foot cone of pyroclastic rocks occupied, in the space of 9 years, a large area of what previously had been fertile farm land.

G. P. Kuiper has estimated the thickness of the Imbrian lava-flows to be from 20 to 200 metres and the lengths may be as much as 200 kilometres (125 miles). J. Green, a well-known geologist, in similar context has referred to the thicknesses of terrestrial lava flows and states that some are only a few metres deep, and flows more than 90 metres deep are rare. He has given a few examples: the lava flows of the Columbia Plateau in the north-western United States are probably less than 15 metres deep: in India basaltic flows average less than 18 metres, and in Iceland the average thickness varies from about 4 to 9 metres. The actual areas involved may be anything from a few acres to many square miles. In Iceland one flow is reported to be more than 1000 square kilometres (400 square miles) in extent. If there are lava flows on the Moon as profound as 200 metres they would be deeper than any so far discovered on the Earth.

G. P. Kuiper has also described colour differences between individual Imbrian lava flows and points out that the oldest appear to be the "reddest". This should not be interpreted as meaning that we should see red patches on the Moon through our telescopes—lunar colours are very difficult to observe except in one or two well-known areas, and, in his search for them, the astronomer uses both photographic and photometric equipment with special coloured filters for isolating those regions of the spectrum in which he wishes to conduct his investigations.

Although all lunar maria are not of the same hue, it is reasonably certain that they have common origins, and if lava flows can be identified definitely in one of them this would seem to dispel any lingering doubts about the others and their volcanic beginnings.

Coupled with colours is the question of albedo that we have considered in Chapter 4. Selenologists can produce powerful reasons for believing that the brightest objects on the lunar surface are the most recent: these features include Aristarchus, Tycho, Copernicus and many other smaller craters on the visible hemisphere whose ray systems obliterate the underlying crustal formations. Most of the bright objects occupy the so-called continental or upland regions of the Moon, and those that do not, e.g. Aristarchus, Copernicus and Kepler, may have been excavated from continental material that has been submerged beneath a comparatively thin layer of the darker material of the maria. For example, if we continue the Oceanus Procellarum basin, both Aristarchus and Kepler could be located on a lightly submerged astronautical eastern wall. Likewise Copernicus is not to be found in the centre of a mare: there are no bright large objects in the central areas of any of the maria. We do not know enough about this subject so it is to be hoped that until we do no one will argue against the author coupling together all of the brighter craters and calling them "continental" in origin.

Having done this, we may consider the maria where we have the seeming contradiction that the darkest areas appear to be the most recent. For example, we can find dark spots of a few kilometres in diameter, usually containing central craters, that intrude right into the ray systems. We have mentioned the three in the immediate environs of Copernicus that have broken through the ray structure—if we do not admit that this has happened we have to postulate a deployment of Copernican rays that covered everything in the area save the three spots, and this is even more difficult to believe. There are three more very prominent spots of similar character within the ramparts of Alphonsus—these, in fact, plus the gas emissions reported by Kosyrev, supplied sufficient reason for making this crater the target of Ranger 9.

As it turned out, not only was the mission of Ranger 9 perfectly planned and executed, but the choice of target was also a wise one because Alphonsus contains some of the most interesting selenological exhibits that fall into the following classifications:

1. Smooth bright central peak.
2. Irregular ridge running from north to south through the centre.
3. Extensive rille system.
4. Collapse features.
5. Craters and craterlets in large numbers.
6. Dark haloed craters.
7. Ancient eroded craters and depressions.

If we examine a full Moon photograph, Alphonsus can be instantly recognized by the three dark patches or haloes that contain small craters. These form near enough a right-angled triangle with the hypotenuse facing towards Copernicus. With the exception of the three dark areas and the bright central peak the remainder of the formation possesses a brightness similar to that of its surroundings to the north and south as well as to the east. On the western edge the continental material vanishes abruptly and is replaced by a smooth, dark, irregular-shaped area that, if anything, resembles the profile of a parrot pecking into the western rampart of Alphonsus. The head of this parrot is larger than Alphonsus and it is attached to a body that extends in the direction of Copernicus, also there is a plume on the head that points in the direction of Tycho. There are three small bright craters in the head and one in the body. Digressing briefly, on the opposite side of Alphonsus there is a sizeable crater named Parrot in honour of Johann Parrot who had a somewhat varied career, during the course of which he was a staff surgeon in the Russian Army in 1815, a professor of physiology and pathology in 1821, and in 1826 he was made a professor of physics at Dorpat.

Returning to our subject, when we examine the Ranger 9 photographs, especially those that show Alphonsus and the dark parrot shape adjacent to it (see Plate 3), and the camera A photographs taken from a height of 236 miles and some 3 minutes to impact show both areas clearly, one of the first things that strikes the observer is the disparity in the populations of small craters in the two areas. In the first instance Alphonsus is liberally peppered with craters and craterlets that can be found in ever-increasing numbers as the close-up pictures are examined. The dark area cannot be examined under close-up conditions because there are no such pictures in the Ranger 9 series; however, the more distant shots indicate that comparatively few craters are to be found in the dark area.

Several agencies could be responsible for this phenomenon. Firstly, in the absence of well-defined crater-chains hinting at vulcanism one could classify these Alphonsus craters and craterlets as being of secondary origin and by-products of the Tycho ray system: many of the less prominent elements of the Tycho ray system are found in this region of the Moon. Some of these elements can be traced to the southern shores of the dark "parrot head" whence they disappear. Their abrupt cessation poses a question: did they really cease so abruptly or did they at one time extend across the dark area? If the latter is the case where are they now? If we take these facts at face value we have little recourse but to admit that the most likely explanation is that the dark "parrot head" is of more recent origin than the Tycho rays, and Tycho itself is reckoned by some authorities to be one of the most youthful of lunar formations. A less acceptable explanation might be found if it were established that the dark area consists of materials hard enough to resist secondary impacts, but, even if this were so, we would expect to be able to observe where the brighter material had smashed itself to powder without necessarily excavating the harder material. No, the most reasonable assertion is that the dark "parrot head" is post-Tychonian, a fact that would also account for the small crater population within it.

Another interesting item emerges after we have scrutinized the close-up photographs of the dark haloed craters inside Alphonsus (see Plate 4). Here we have direct evidence of dark material ejected around each crater to cover existing craterlets and fill rilles in the immediate neighbourhood. Thus we have what seems to be proof of Plutonic activity in Alphonsus. How else can we account for the three separate dark areas intruding into a large region characterized by its brightness? Furthermore, unless we invoke some impossibly selective manner in which to deploy the small craterlets within Alphonsus, we cannot escape from the conclusion that the darker material covered and filled them within the haloed areas. The same may also be said of the rilles, for it can be no accident that these too have become shallow and in some cases completely filled up in the environment of each haloed crater.

On this basis it would appear that Alphonsus is an old formation for, in addition to the many newer craterlets that the author has associated with Tycho, there are multitudes of older ones that appear smoother and more eroded and which may well represent the original configuration of the pre-Tychonian floor of Alphonsus. On the acceptance that this represents a true history of the formation we can at least sketch out several distinct phases in its development:

1. Excavation of original formation and subsequent filling with mare-type material. Original colour of the floor would be dark grey. Whether or not the initial excavation was made by internal or external explosive forces is not known. Perhaps more likely it came into being as a caldera which may be either a collapse or explosive feature.

2. Formation of floor craters by meteoric impact and also by secondary impacts from the large primary craters.

3. Formation of central ridges by intrusions of magma along zones of weakness.

4. Excavation of Tycho followed by secondary impacts in Alphonsus plus the dusting of the surface sufficient partially to obliterate the original dark grey eroded floor.

5. Because the haloed craters are formed along the rilles it seems permissible to associate the evolution of the two types of feature. Excepting where they are filled with material originating in the haloed craters the rilles are deep and sharp—in other words not badly eroded. The

formation of the haloed craters represents the final stage in the development of Alphonsus.

As far as the author can see—he is not so naïve as to expect that everyone will agree with him—this provides an acceptable outline of the sequence of events following the excavation of Alphonsus. As for the origin itself, nearly every selenologist has his own ideas. Even the Earth itself may not have been just a passive by-stander for the Earth tides would assume considerable proportions in fluid magma flows near the centre of the Moon's disc. Regarding the 3500-foot central peak, the Ranger photographs do not show any evidence that favours a volcanic cone with a central crater; it is, however, a bright object and is evidently composed of, or coated with, a different material to the floor (see Plate 5). G. P. Kuiper has suggested that it is covered with a whitish evaporate—possibly as a result of recent gaseous activity. Another point of view that has often been argued, but not necessarily endorsed by the author, is that such central peaks are the remnants of the impacting bodies that excavated the craters in the first place, and if this were so in the present case we could explain the difference in brightness on the basis that this material is alien to the Moon.

Lastly we have yet to mention those objects that, for the want of a better name, have been described within these pages as gouge-type valleys. These seem to be older features of Plutonic origin that in some instances suggest the appearance of blocked rilles: they may also be classified as pre-Tychonian objects because they are found in those areas of the floor that are covered with Tycho ray material. Most likely, like the rilles that have been measured in Manchester by Z. Kopal and his staff and that are now known to have depths of about 80 or 90 metres, they may be collapse features. So in this case we may imagine deep fissures opening up in the subsurface rocks into which the overlying and loosely agglomerated material slumped. On the other hand, some low-angle illumination photography taken with the 43-inch telescope at the Pic-du-Midi has been investigated by the author, and this suggests that the astronautical eastern floor, in the neighbourhood of the largest rille on which is found two of the haloed craters, actually rises. This might be interpreted as a manifestation of pressure from below pushing up and fracturing the surface rocks so that the rille actually runs along the top of a low ridge.

Far away from the ramparts of Alphonsus there are other features that suggest vulcanism to some of those who try to solve the lunar hieroglyphs. These are the chains of small craters that were well known to selenographers long before the age of astronautics. A typical chain may consist of half a dozen or more small craters, each almost overlapping the next to form a linear configuration across the lunar crust. There is a fine example of a crater-chain on the astronautical north-eastern wall of Ptolemaeus.

It has been pointed out by J. Green that crater-chains are also fairly common on the Earth and they frequently occur where there are linear zones of weakness that, from time to time, are replenished with subterranean lava. Aligned craterlets of this description may be found in the Jordan Valley, also in the State of Oregon and at Lakagígar in Iceland. To compare terrestrial formations of this type with their lunar counterparts, though popular with the geologists, is a dangerous and ill-lit road to pursue because of the very large-scale differences involved. In the case of lunar crater-chains the lines of weakness in many cases seem to follow the hexagonal walls of large craters and ringed plains: certainly with the Ptolemaeus example the crater-chain does seem to be an extrapolation of the north-eastern wall, and the fact that there are many other similarly aligned crater-chains on the lunar surface tends, at first sight, to demolish the arguments of those who postulate the formation of crater-chains as a result of sticks of meteorites falling like bombs upon the Moon. Like the bombs of World War II that so often were reported as having been dropped at random, these meteoritic lunar crater-chains would seem to require a randomness in their deployment that might be difficult to substantiate. On the other hand, if there are linear "subselenean" cavities close to the surface, a random hail of meteorites over long periods of time might cause their collapse and still produce appearances of a linear crater-chains.

The close-up photographs of the lunar crust have revealed "rib" features that suggest vulcanism to some investigators. If these are not just due to the misinterpretation of the photographs—it was pointed out by D. R. Gault, H. J. Moore *et al.*, that certain features that were thought to be volcanic flow fronts were found to be crests of ridges after the pictures of Lunik 9 had been reviewed stereoscopically—if, as we said, these items are raised "ribs" we could account for them on the assumption that they are intrusions of magma into existing fissures. After solidification they could form harder rock than that in which they are moulded, and subsequent erosion could remove the softer rock and leave the harder vein standing proud of the surface. We shall return to the question of erosion in the section that follows.

Lunar Erosion

Earlier in this book some discussion has been devoted to micrometeoritic impacts on the lunar surface and the possible effects of such collisions. We have now reached the point where we can reopen these discussions by demanding if the Ranger, Lunik or Surveyor photography has supplied us with any additional evidence in support or denial of this hypothesis. Have these cameras glimpsed anything pertinent to this subject that can help us make up our minds?

Some sort of start can be made from the undeniable fact that micrometeoroids continue to arrive in the Earth–Moon environs and should therefore be incident upon both bodies. This is why the apparent absence of loose lunar dust caused such a stir in selenological circles. For up-to-date information on micrometeoritic fluxes we can now use the counts obtained from satellites. One enormous 70-foot-long American satellite, Pegasus 3, weighing 23,100 pounds, was launched from Cape Kennedy on 30th July, 1965 and took up a nearly circular orbit at a height of just over 400 miles above the Earth. Up to 21st December—more than $4\frac{1}{2}$

months later—the following micrometeoroidal counts had been registered: 59 hits on 16-mil (0·016-inch) panels: 14 on 8-mil (0·008-inch) panels: 123 on 1·5-mil (0·0015-inch) panels. The preliminary Pegasus report published by NASA reveals that the flux of larger particles was greater than expected and the flux of the smallest was less. The 8-mil expectations were confirmed. On the Pegasus the total area of the detection panels for all sizes of micrometeorite was 2300 square feet, and this leads us to some interesting speculations despite the fact that there is no way of proving, or for that matter, disproving them. If we round off the total number of recorded impacts to 200 for this $4\frac{1}{2}$-month period this is equivalent to a frequency of one hit per square metre per $4\frac{1}{2}$ months which is not a very exciting result (unless one happens to be an astronaut destined to go to the Moon). Nevertheless, if— and there are quite a few "ifs" in this calculation—if we assume that each impact corresponds to a kinetic energy of approximately 5×10^4 erg (50,000 ergs) which is a figure suggested by F. L. Whipple for particles of about 5-mil (0·005-inch) diameter—here we are being a little biased in favour of the smaller and more numerous particles—then, on the improbable basis that the flux of micrometeorites has not changed significantly throughout the entire life of the Moon, we can calculate the number of hits and the energy involved. Let us say that one impact per square meter per $4\frac{1}{2}$ months is close enough to three hits per year. This over $4\frac{1}{2}$ aeons—the age of the Moon—is no less than 13,500 million impacts per square metre. By applying Whipple's energy estimate and converting it to electrical power that most people know something about since they have to pay for it with monotonous regularity, the total power is a little less than 70,000 kilowatts. In terms of electrical heating this would keep a 1-kilowatt fire going for 24 hours of each day for 42 weeks. The same amount of electricity would keep a 1-horse-power motor operating continuously for more than one year, and if the spindle of such a motor were fitted with a sharp grindstone we might be able to imagine the havoc that could be wrought on a 1-metre square area of silicate rock during this period of time.

This, then, is a very rough-and-ready calculation which may be seriously in error, for many astronomers believe that the fluxes of micrometeoroids were very much greater in the far remote past. Nevertheless, it serves its purpose by indicating the very large amounts of power that are generated by feeble mechanisms over extremely long periods of time.

To the erosive forces of micrometeorites we must add those caused by solar radiation, particularly protons that are released by solar flares and the rarer cosmic events. Certainly there will be radiation damage done to the lunar rocks resulting in a darkening that has been demonstrated in terrestrial laboratories under simulated conditions. In addition, heavy fluxes of solar protons can stimulate luminescence that has been observed through ground-based telescopes.

There are all sorts of other phenomena that could be caused by the solar wind or radiation, but most of them are ideas on paper describing physical realities that have yet to be discovered on the Moon.

This really brings us back to the original question. Does any of the close-up photography furnish evidence that favours erosive processes on the Moon? The answer must certainly be in the affirmative, and not only does the evidence stem from the two soft-landers; the Ranger close-up material also indicated that erosive forces had been at work.

Firstly we have the testimony of the large numbers of rounded and virtually rimless depressions, many of which contain smaller and sharply defined craterlets with rims. There are not too many facts that we can assert absolutely in lunar matters, but we encounter one of them here: formations that contain others must be older than the ones they contain, for, after all, the former supplies the material from which the latter are made.

In the case of the ancient rimless depressions most of the original rampart material may have fallen back into the interior possibly assisted by Gold's electrostatic dust transport mechanism, or again, the sharp outlines of the older craters may have been softened by a partial remelting of the surface material. Either

PLATE 6.

The lunar rock shown in this composite picture was photographed by the television camera of Surveyor 1 on 3rd June,
1966. The rock is approximately 6 inches high and 18 inches
long. NASA photograph.

PLATE 7.

The indentation of Surveyor 1's footpad on the lunar surface is well shown in this computer-enhanced photograph. The surface is seen to consist of granular material in the dimensional range of a few centimetres down to the limits of resolution of the camera lens. NASA photograph.

PLATE 8.

The interior of the crater, Copernicus, as recorded by the cameras of Lunar Orbiter 2 in November 1966. The central peaks and the precipitous northern ramparts are shown in detail while, beyond, can be seen parts of the Carpathian Mountain Range. A description of this photograph appears on pages 158-9.   NASA photograph.

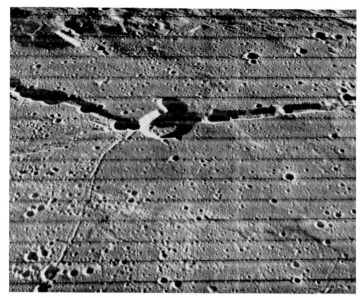

PLATE 9.

This remarkable photograph of the Hyginus crater and associated rilles was secured by Orbiter 3 that was launched on 4th February 1967. The camera was pointing north. Most of the smaller features shown here are beyond the photographic resolving limits of earth-based telescopes. NASA photograph.

or both of these agencies may have played their part but, of the two, surface erosion seems the most likely.

In the close-up photography from the soft-landing probes the broken, jagged and irregular surface that we now see may have been originally a comparatively smooth surface that has since suffered severe erosion. There are at least two variations of this theme:

1. *Accretion.* Micrometeoroidal building of the lunar crust by impact welding. This, on the Earth, is comparable to the building of a coral reef in that the structure is a positive or elevated one attached to the underlying surface rocks. If this sort of process has been happening throughout the Moon's life this may have resulted in a slight increase in the diameter of the lunar globe accompanied by an increase in the mass.

2. *Erosion.* The opposite viewpoint to the above is that the kinetic energy of impacting particles from space is sufficient to remove mass from the Moon. A useful way to imagine this is to think of each impact as an explosive force capable of excavating existing lunar material and launching it away from the Moon at speeds in excess of escape velocity. To allow the Moon to lose mass by this process we have to assert that the mass so released is larger than that of the impacting grain. Instead of building upwards this process would tend to excavate existing lunar rocks and it would be selective in the sense that the softer lunar rocks would be removed more quickly than the harder materials. This type of erosion could produce the raised ribs of the intruded dikes that were briefly described earlier in this chapter. Coupled with the same question, and suggestive of erosive forces, are the stony objects that are said to stand slightly above the lunar surface on rocky pedestals. If these objects exist, and the author has not been able to recognize them in the Lunik 9 and Surveyor 1 photography, the inference is that the harder upper rock has resisted erosion while its softer "stalk" has been gradually worn away by the micrometeoroidal impacts arriving from all directions. "Stalks" or not, there are plenty of small rocks to be seen that range in size from about 50 centimetres downwards—in the

M.I.F.—F

immediate environment of Lunik 9 there were some about 15 centimetres in length—but how they arrived there is another mystery. Were they fragments ejected from craters or have they arrived from outer space? Are they loose or are they cemented to the surface? We do not have long to wait for the answers.

As for the surface itself there is no unanimity among the experts. Some take the view that the surface, despite its grainy and broken appearance, is solid in the sense that one could cut out a massive slab of it and bring it back to Earth. The opposite view is that it is composed of loosely agglomerated material of a cindery or slaggy character. So, instead of bringing back a slab, we may one day be confronted at the breakfast table by newspaper pictures showing astronauts bearing sacks on their backs like celestial coal merchants.

The Ranger 9 close-up photographs of the central peak of Alphonsus reveal that this object is not only brighter but less pitted and seemingly smoother than the surrounding floor. Parts of the outer walls of Alphonsus also show similar brightness and texture, and our first reaction is to explain this disparity between the elevations and the floor in terms of rock differences. A well-known geologist, J. E. Spurr, in the early 1940's coined the words "lunarite" and "lunabase" to help him differentiate between the highlands and the plains. The question that arises from this is whether the central peak of Alphonsus, in keeping with many other central peaks and isolated mountains such as Piton and Pico, is made of different material to the surrounding floor. If it is of similar chemical composition why the difference in albedo or brightness? For one explanation we can return directly to Gold's dust-migration hypothesis. Let us suppose that the central peak is made of the same material as the surrounding floor of Alphonsus, and that their ages are the same. Let us further suppose that the solar wind has been darkening these rocks. Why, then, are they not of the same brightness: why is the peak much brighter than the floor? Of course we cannot provide an answer but this need not stop us pondering these problems, and coming up with more questions. Are the erosive forces of micrometeoroids responsible and, if so, is this a process that works more efficiently on steeply sloping surfaces? If the answer is yes, we may then envisage a continuous sand-blasting effect that removes the radiation-damaged and darkened rock and maintains the pristine brightness of the central peak by the constant renewal of the surface. The dust and debris slides down the slopes to the foot of the peak. It may be nothing more than coincidence but a Ranger 9 camera A photograph (Plate 5) taken from a height of about 55 miles and 36·7 seconds to impact shows two patches of whitish material that seem to have spilled out over the floor at the foot of the central peak. If this is indeed eroded material from the peak this raises another question. Why should the erstwhile darkened material reaching the foot of the peak now appear to be white? We can think of two possibilities: firstly, any rock that has been finely ground will be lighter in colour than the solid from which it comes. Secondly, Gold has demonstrated that radiation-damaged rock powders can be restored to their former brightness by heating. Micrometeoroids arriving on the Moon at speeds of 10 – 20 miles per second could hardly hit anything without causing localized heating, so there are two interrelated processes here to which we may add a third that the darkening process is also dependent on the contaminants in the rock, a fact that may help in the dating of the lunar rocks.

Final Summary

Let us take one brief appraisal of the lunar globe as a whole. Firstly, there can be no doubt that the Moon is an extremely complex body whose crustal rocks bear the record of many physical processes. We can list some of the forces involved, but it is very certain that others remain to be discovered:

1. Macrometeoroidal impacts.
2. Vulcanism.
3. Micrometeoroidal impacts.
4. Solar wind and protonic showers.

There is no division between 1 and 3 except that we can think of 1 as being a moulding process and 3 as a smoothing or erosive process, that, if given millions of years to operate, can efface some features completely and materially change the shapes and appearances of others. Ray systems can also be obliterated by such forces.

Vulcanism, or at least some sort of internal process in the body of the Moon, must be accepted—or should we say reaccepted, since it has always been a current theory in one form or another—this may help to explain the absence of water on the Moon. On the Earth, water and steam are necessary to volcanic processes—in fact it is the steam pressure that does much of the damage in explosions like the classic Krakatoa explosion on the fateful 27th August, 1883.

There are other types of rock that cannot be present on the lunar surface—these are the sedimentary rocks like limestone and chalk that are found so abundantly on the Earth. They are composed largely of calcium carbonate and are, as everyone knows, the fossilized remains of small marine creatures that lived millions of years ago. We have no reason to believe that the Moon ever went through a parallel phase when life might have emerged. The complete absence of anything remotely akin to a breatheable atmosphere, the lack of water, and the lethal solar radiations make it absolutely certain that no forms of life could exist, let alone evolve in such hostile surroundings. Thus we can state with some assurance that there are no sedimentary rocks that have been compacted out of the remains of once-living creatures.

The author is not going to pretend that he has exhausted a fraction of the information that is steadily becoming available. It is fairly certain that other exciting discoveries will be made before this book finds itself in the shops. The story that is being unfolded here is more like a serial with other episodes forthcoming in the near future. Also it is a story without end for we have observed how each new item of information leads to further unanswerable questions. It seems that every time we take a step forward we retreat at least two.

An attempt has been made within these pages to bring the Moon into focus, and the author is conscious of certain image blurrings and imperfections that still persist and that are due to inadequate information—these will disappear like vapour from a spectacle lens in the course of time. Some readers who already have some acquaintance with the Moon may be disappointed to read that the new version looks very much like the old one they used to know before the advent of the space probes. But if this is so, they ought to find some satisfaction in the knowledge that the older selenologists knew their subject and wrote books that are not yet out of date, for much of what has been written over the years has not changed. The major breakthrough in the lunar defences has been achieved by the hard- and soft-landed space probes whose photographs have unveiled the small-scale structure of the lunar surface as we now know it. To the newcomer the author extends an earnest invitation to observe and discover for himself the fascination of the Moon through the magic world of the telescope. A small telescope and the chart in the back of this volume are the only tools required. And while he is partaking of these pleasures he should spare a thought for the astronomers on their mountain peaks and in other remote parts of the world, who, together with the vast army of scientists, lunar-charting experts, technicians and workers of a thousand-and-one industries, are co-operating to assemble the words that will write the most exciting chapter of all—Man on the Moon.

Postscript

WITH any printed work there is always a delay following the submission of the author's manuscript and the day of publication, when for the first time the book is offered to its readers. Such a delay, no matter how short, constitutes a period in which events continue to happen, and some interesting and important developments in astronautics as applied to lunar research have occurred since the author wrote the final chapter of this book. In a sense, some of the postscript that follows is a continuation of Chapters 6 and 7, for here we are mainly concerned with the space probes and their findings.

Let us resume our survey of the American Lunar Orbiter 1, the technicalities of which were described at the end of Chapter 6 and which was launched on 10th August, 1966 and eventually placed in a circumlunar orbit possessing a perilune of 188 kilometres and an apolune of 1860 kilometres. The perilune was reduced to 58 kilometres on 21st August and the photography of nine possible Apollo landing sites was started on the following day. Unfortunately spurious radio signals triggered the shutter of the high-resolution camera (lens: 24-inch $f/5\cdot6$) and caused some blurring of the finer detail. The medium-resolution camera performed as planned and Lunar Orbiter 1 was able to accomplish about 75% of its mission.

It has been reported that some 12 days were needed to relay all of the photographic information back to Earth, where it was recorded on some 8 miles of 35-millimetre film. In addition to close-up photography of possible Apollo landing sites along the normally visible equatorial regions of the lunar disc other frames revealed wonderful detail of areas in the averted hemisphere. One particularly striking photograph shows a terminator region of continental structure possessing large overlapping rings of up to 60 or 80 kilometres in diameter. These are so full of smaller craters of all diameters down to about 10 metres—the limit of resolution—that it seems unlikely that any part of the entire area could yield a surface sufficiently plane for the landing of a lunar module. Never before has the selenologist perceived such an irregular surface; but even here it is not without order, for it is possible to observe the non-random deployment of small craters in sinuous chains.

Dramatic and magnificent as these photographs are it is nevertheless true that Lunar Orbiter 1, in the years to come, will be remembered chiefly for the photographs it secured during its 16th orbit at 16 hours 36 minutes U.T. on 23rd August, 1966. These are the much publicized photographs showing the crescent Earth setting behind a great sweep of the bright lunar horizon. The area of lunar surface contained in this montage is more than 300,000 square kilometres, but owing to the curvature of the lunar sphere the areas close to the horizon are very foreshortened. Despite this the camera has recorded a wealth of lunar detail which, since the Earth appears in the same view, proves that it is confined to the normally averted lunar hemisphere. The more usual features include several fine ringed plains with diameters of up to 100 kilometres as well as smaller craters and craterlets in great profusion down to the resolving limits of the cameras. In addition to these there are also unusual features, some of which were seen in the Russian Zond 3 photographs secured in July 1965. These have been classified by Russian astronomers as "thalassoids" and may be described as deep mare-type depressions possessing no prominent raised rims but having unsmooth light floors containing large numbers of craters, irregularities and faults. Russian astronomers suppose that the differences between thalassoids and maria can be explained if we accept the view that all maria originated as thalassoids, and that at some later stage magma flooded the floors to reduce their depths and to provide the smooth dark areas we observe today. The Zond 3 photographs show thalassoids that have diameters of more than 500 kilometres: that shown in the Orbiter 1 photograph is about 200 kilometres across. Curiously enough these objects are confined to the averted hemisphere, but quasi-thalassoidal features such as Janssen and Clavius can be observed on the hemisphere that is normally accessible to terrestrial telescopes. Other unusual objects that seem to be more numerous on the averted hemisphere are the deep conical craters of up to 30 or 40 kilometres diameter that are also shown in the Orbiter photograph. It is an interesting photograph in many ways, for the illumination and aspect together yield a panorama that with the exercise of some imagination could be almost of terrestrial origin: it is quite unlike the normal lunar surface seen through Earth-based telescopes.

The geometry of this particular montage is also unique, for the terrestrial latitude and longitude of the Moon have been given as 22°·91 S. and 24°·06 E., respectively. In other words the Moon would have been observed at the zenith in the Kalahari Desert in South Africa. Simultaneously the Sun's zenith position was over Maracaibo, Venezuela, in latitude 11°·52 N. and longitude 291°·35 E. of the Greenwich meridian. Thus, at this epoch, the Sun and Moon were separated by 92°·71 in geographical longitude; hence the Moon as seen from the Earth was at first quarter, and the Earth, as photographed by Orbiter from a height of 1197 kilometres above the lunar surface, was at last quarter. This aspect of the Earth claims particular attention by virtue of the large amount of cloud cover recorded which gives our planet an appearance not unlike a telescopic view of Venus. On the original copies of this photograph one may trace some of the North African coastline and, had it not been hidden by cloud, all of the African continent west of longitude 24° E. One of the most prominent features on the terrestrial image is the great hurricane complex that dominated the south Atlantic before moving into the Gulf of Mexico to cause damage and loss of human life: such photography eloquently underlines the potential value of meteorological stations based on the Moon.

Lunar Orbiter 1 continued to encircle the Moon for more than 2 months, and after its film supplies had been exhausted it used its telemetry system to relay to Earth information concerning the lunar gravitational field and the fluxes of radiation and micrometeoroids in the lunar vicinity. Eventually, and on the receipt of a command from Earth, Lunar Orbiter 1 was deflected from its orbit by a 97-second ignition of a small rocket and it crashed on the averted hemisphere at 13.30 hours U.T. on 29th October, 1966. The wrecked space probe's position has been given as longitude 162° E. and latitude 6°·7 N. and it was made to crash to prevent its transmitters from interfering with signals from those of other space-craft.

Long before Lunar Orbiter 1 met its fate in the averted hemisphere other space probes had been despatched. The Russian Lunik 11 launched on 24th August, 1966 achieved a circumlunar orbit, and on 20th September the American Surveyor 2 started its ill-fated voyage that ended in a crash landing in the Oceanus Procellarum. One month later, on 22nd October, Russian space probe Lunik 12 soared away from the Earth to become yet another lunar orbiter. So far very little information has been released about the findings of the two Russian orbiters.

Following Lunik 12 by 2 weeks came the launching of American Lunar Orbiter 2 at 23.21 hours U.T. on 6th November, 1966. The Atlas–Agena rocket placed the vehicle in a parking orbit some 185 kilometres above the terrestrial surface and the Agena was fired for the second time 11 minutes afterwards to provide sufficient thrust to send Orbiter 2 towards the Moon. Later a midcourse manoeuvre increased its velocity by 2·5% to 3060 kilometres per hour and the space probe achieved a circumlunar orbit on 10th November with a perilune of 209 kilometres and an apolune of 1850 kilometres.

For the 5 days that followed Lunar Orbiter 2 was used as a passive probe for the study of the lunar gravitational field which, in turn, led to a better knowledge of the shape of the Moon. Subsequently at 22.58 hours U.T. on 15th November a small rocket motor was fired to modify the shape of the orbit and the perilune distance was changed to 50 kilometres without affecting the apolune. At this time the orbital period was 3 hours 28 minutes. Lunar photography with the medium-resolution Xenotar 80-millimetre $f/5\cdot6$ and the high-resolution Paxoramic 24-inch $f/5\cdot6$ lenses was initiated on 18th and continued until 25th November, 1966. A 200-foot roll of 70-millimetre film provided emulsion space for 211 pictures from each camera, among them sample frames to check the performance of the photographic system. Telemetry transmissions ceased prematurely on 6th December, but by this time 97% of the photographic information had been relayed back to Earth.

One of the principal tasks of the Lunar Orbiter 2 was to obtain close-up photography of thirteen selected areas in the equatorial regions of maria where possible Apollo landing sites might be chosen. In the list below longitudes without sign are positive and those with the negative prefix are astronautically west of the central meridian, i.e. in the same hemisphere as the large crater Copernicus.

Lunar Orbiter 2

List of possible Apollo landing sites

Site	Longitude (degrees)	Latitude (degrees)	Region
1	37·0	4·2	Mare Tranquillitatis
2	37·0	2·8	Mare Tranquillitatis
3	21·4	4·4	Mare Tranquillitatis
4	15·7	4·8	Ariadaeus Rille
5	24·8	2·6	Mare Tranquillitatis
6	24·0	0·8	Mare Tranquillitatis
7	−2·0	2·2	Sinus Medii
8	−1·0	0	Sinus Medii
9	−13·0	1·0	Near Gambart
10	−27·1	3·5	Near Lansberg
11	−20·0	0	Near Gambart A
12	−34·6	2·4	Near Encke
13	−42·2	1·5	Near Encke

Near site no. 11 the cameras of Orbiter 2 recorded in excellent detail the lunar surface in and around the great bowl of Copernicus. One photograph, exposed when the space probe was crossing the lunar equator south of Copernicus at approximately perilune height, shows a remarkable vista that stretches away to the horizon which is about 400 kilometres to the north. A very foreshortened Copernicus can be seen, but this is still 225 kilometres from the camera. Closer, at a distance of 105 kilometres, the small though deep double crater, Fauth, dominates the view. Between it and the closest details visible to the camera the lunar surface is fairly smooth but nevertheless interrupted by numerous features that come into the following classifications:

1. *Domes*. There is one well-defined dome in the foreground and several others that are smaller and more irregular in its immediate environs.
2. *Crater-chains*. There are many of these. One of the best starts astronautically east of Fauth and follows a sinuous path to the north-east where it is crossed (or crosses) other crater-chains coming in from the east. There seems to be no marked division between the small craters and the elongated valleys that together form the most prominent features of these chains.
3. *Craterlets*. As would be expected from the findings of the Rangers the Copernican area has large numbers of craterlets down to the resolving limits of the camera lenses.
4. *Shallow circular depressions*. Many of these are displayed in this photograph. It seems reasonable to suppose that they are ancient features that have been eroded by micrometeoroidal infall.
5. *Copernicus H*. Earlier in this book reference was made to several craters that are surrounded by dark haloes that intrude into the Copernican ray system. Copernicus H is one of the best examples and it can be seen at the extreme right (astronautically east) of this Orbiter 2 photograph. The author's opinion that such features are more recent in

origin than the ray system that surrounds them is further strengthened by the appearance of the crater, which is very symmetrical and sharply defined. The best terrestrial telescopic photographs show that it is almost perfectly circular, and the Orbiter photograph's oblique view reveals that it has steeply inclined outer slopes, a sharp rim and a deep regular interior. Evidently erosive forces have not had enough time to moderate the appearance of this crater, which probably testifies to an age of no more than a few million years.

Another photograph (Plate 8) from the same series was exposed when the selenographic coordinates of Orbiter 2 were approximately longitude 21°W., latitude 4°N., which means that the probe was east of the crater Reinhold. Some quite lofty peaks in the Carpathanian Mountains and the Gay Lussac area dominate the horizon, and in the immediate foreground the camera plumbs the steep concavity of Fauth. Despite this, it is the intermediate area containing a large expanse of the floor and northern walls of Copernicus that claims the greatest attention. The inner northern wall contains precipitous ground, but the mean slope from the rim to the interior floor was measured by the author a few years ago and was found to be about 10°. There is an abrupt and fairly smooth drop from the rim of about 1000 metres to the interior elevations that tumble gently down to the central floor. To the east it is possible to see evidence of internal radial ridges and there are others to the west that are less radial and more sinuous in character. Small craters are difficult to detect, for on this northern wall they are still 140–160 kilometres away from the camera.

The southern internal wall must have a similar appearance but, as viewed by Orbiter's cameras, it is far less dramatic. This is merely an effect of camera angle for, from the crater rim, Orbiter was about 20° above the horizon at the time of the exposure, so that it "looked" down a very foreshortened 10° slope of the inner southern ramparts.

The central peaks of Copernicus are, for the most part, smooth and ridgy, but one of them displays three hemispherical blocks that range from about 300–400 metres in diameter high up on the slope and about 500 metres below the ridged summit. These features run in a short line approximately parallel to the floor of Copernicus and they may be harder rocky formations that have resisted the lunar erosional processes. On the eastern slope of the same mountain there exists what may be called a continuation of these features: this seems to take the form of a wide vein of rock that runs from the summit to the floor and which is about 400 metres wide. This seam of apparently hard rock stands proud of its surroundings by about 30 metres near the summit to about 100 metres at the base. If this feature is what it appears to be it could indicate stratification and subsequent tilting of the lunar crustal rocks.

The eastern and southern parts of the floor of Copernicus contain low hummocky hills ranging in height from a few tens to a few hundreds of metres. Small craters can be found, but the impression generally is that of a hilly surface rather than a predominantly cratered one. To the west the floor is very much smoother with a few isolated low hills and a spattering of almost rimless depressions.

These are brief descriptions of a few of the Orbiter 1 and 2 frames that have been released by the Boeing Corporation and NASA for general circulation. There are hundreds of others that are in the process of being analysed; while Orbiters 3, 4 and 5 are expected to swell the number by approximately 1200.

A great deal of work is being done in other fields and J. M. Saari and R. W. Shorthill of the Boeing Corporation, who have made a detailed study of the lunar thermal properties, have pointed out that Surveyor 1's temperature sensors transmitted to Earth signals that indicated that the temperature of the space-probe's environment closely approximated to the computed temperature and was not very different from that derived from their own ground-based measurements. At local noon the temperature reached 390°K (117° C) and dropped to about 170° K

(−103° C) at sunset. The same investigators ascribe their observed thermal anomalies on the lunar surface to variations in the porosity and deployment of surface rocks and materials.

Brief mention has been made of the Orbiters being used as passive probes to monitor the lunar gravitational field, and an analysis of the perturbations performed by C. L. Goudas, Z. Kopal and Z. Kopal have led to a determination of the principal properties of the gravitational field that in turn permits (assuming certain premises) the shape of the Moon to be calculated. It is interesting to observe that a harmonic analysis performed on data obtained from lunar negatives measured at the Aeronautical Chart and Information Center of the U.S. Air Force has yielded results that agree well with those obtained from the orbit of Orbiter 1. These authors state that while there are local heights on the Moon that exceed 2·2 kilometres it is unlikely that departures from sphericity are going to exceed this value over large areas. They conclude that the lunar globe has sufficient mechanical strength to sustain such departures and that the lunar crust would seem to be more rigid than its terrestrial counterpart.

The material described in these pages refers to only a small fraction of the work that is proceeding at an ever-increasing tempo towards the final goal of understanding the physical properties of the Moon. Even if technological progress limits its rate to that of the last decade who can tell what interplanetary discovery will reveal within the next century?

By way of conclusion the author has assembled a table that lists the lunar space probes in chronological order, with their respective country of origin, type of vehicle (i.e. O—orbiter; H—hard-lander; S—soft-lander; F—fly-by). Also given, where possible, is the astronautical longitude and latitude of each impact on the Moon. Space has been provided for readers to extend this list as new information comes in.

Vehicle	Date	Origin	Type	Long. Lat. (degrees)
Lunik 1	1959 January 2	U.S.S.R.	F	
Lunik 2	1959 September 12	U.S.S.R.	H	0 30 N.
Lunik 3	1959 October 4	U.S.S.R.	F	
Ranger 3	1962 January 26	U.S.A.	F	
Ranger 4	1962 April 23	U.S.A.	H	Impacted on hidden hemisphere
Ranger 5	1962 October 18	U.S.A.	F	
Lunik 4	1963 April 2	U.S.S.R.	F	
Ranger 6	1964 January 30	U.S.A.	H	21·52 E. 9·33 N.
Ranger 7	1964 July 28	U.S.A.	H	20·67 W. 10·70 S.
Ranger 8	1965 February 17	U.S.A.	H	24·60 E. 2·70 N.
Ranger 9	1965 March 21	U.S.A.	H	2·37 W. 12·83 S.
Lunik 5	1965 May 9	U.S.S.R.	H	15·0 W. 28·0 S.
Lunik 6	1965 June 8	U.S.S.R.	F	
Zond 3	1965 July 18	U.S.S.R.	F	
Lunik 7	1965 October 4	U.S.S.R.	H	34·0 W. 8·5 N.
Lunik 8	1965 December 3	U.S.S.R.	H	62·0 W. 9·0 N.
Lunik 9	1966 January 31	U.S.S.R.	S	64·4 W. 7·1 N.
Lunik 10	1966 March 31	U.S.S.R.	O	
Surveyor 1	1966 May 30	U.S.A.	S	43·33 W. 2·37 S.
Orbiter 1	1966 August 10	U.S.A.	O	162·0 E. 6·7 N.
Lunik 11	1966 August 24	U.S.S.R.	O	
Surveyor 2	1966 September 20	U.S.A.	H	0·83 W. 2·37 S.
Lunik 12	1966 October 22	U.S.S.R.	O	
Orbiter 2	1966 November 6	U.S.A.	O	
Lunik 13	1966 December 21	U.S.S.R.	S	62·05 W. 18·87 N.
Orbiter 3	1967 February 4	U.S.A.	O	
Surveyor 3	1967 April 17	U.S.A.	S	23·16 W. 3·33 S.
Orbiter 4	1967 May 4	U.S.A.	O	
Surveyor 4	1967 July 14	U.S.A.	H	
Orbiter 5	1967 August 1	U.S.A.	O	
Surveyor 5	1967 September 8	U.S.A.	S	

Appendix

AN ATTEMPT has been made to tabulate some of the more important quantities relating to the physical aspects of the Moon.

Mass: $7 \cdot 3458 \times 10^{25}$ gram

Mass ratio: $\dfrac{\text{Mass Earth}}{\text{Mass Moon}} = \dfrac{1}{81 \cdot 3} = 0 \cdot 0123.$

Diameter: 2160 miles   3476 kilometres.

Surface area: $4 \cdot 087 \times 10^{14}$ feet$^2 = 14 \cdot 7 \times 10^6$ miles^2.

Volume: $7 \cdot 766 \times 10^{20}$ feet$^3 = 2 \cdot 199 \times 10^{25}$ centimetres^3.

Density: $\dfrac{\text{Mass}}{\text{Volume}} = 3 \cdot 34$ g/cm^3.

Surface acceleration
    due to gravity: $5 \cdot 321$ ft/sec^2 $= 162 \cdot 2$ cm/sec^2

Escape velocity:
      New Moon   8000 ft/sec $= 2440$ m/sec
      Full Moon   7220 ft/sec $= 2204$ m/sec

Earth–Moon distance:
      Perigee   226,426 miles $= 364,397$ kilometres
      Mean   238,857 miles $= 384,402$ kilometres
      Apogee   252,731 miles $= 406,732$ kilometres

Angular diameter
    from Earth   (Topocentric: as seen at zenith from Earth's surface):
      Perigee   33′ 31″·0.
      Mean   31′ 36″·6.
      Apogee   29′ 23″·0.

Photographic magnitude of full Moon: −11·91.

Visual magnitude (5800 Å) of full Moon: −12·5.

Illumination of Earth by full Moon: $1·58 \times 10^{-5}$ lumens/cm².

Named Formations and their Positions

THE lunar chart drawn specially for this book by Antonín Rükl contains 504 named formations in addition to those of the maria, etc. All of these names are approved by the International Astronomical Union, and a full list containing these names and the longitude and latitude of each formation is given in the next few pages. It is hoped that this list will enable the reader to explore the lunar chart as a preliminary to telescopic observations of the Moon. The names of the ocean and seas are listed below:

Oceanus Procellarum
Mare Aestatis
Mare Australe
Mare Cognitum
Mare Crisium
Mare Fecunditatis
Mare Frigoris
Mare Humboltianum
Mare Humorum
Mare Imbrium

Mare Marginus
Mare Nectaris
Mare Nubium
Mare Serenitatis
Mare Smythii
Mare Spumens
Mare Tranquillitatis
Mare Undarum
Mare Vaporum

It is not necessary to provide coordinate data for the above, but some of the maria are not prominent because they are close to the limbs. For example, look for Mare Australe half-way along the limb of quadrant 4, and Mare Smythii on the limb junction of quadrants 4 and 1. Maria Marginus and Humboltianum are located along the limb of quadrant 1. On our clock-face these four positions correspond respectively to approximately 11, 9, 8 and 7 o'clock.

Lakes, marshes and bays are also listed by their Latin names:

	Longitude	Latitude
Lacus Mortis	−27	+45
Lacus Sominiorum	−32	+36
Palus Nebularum	− 5	+38
Palus Putredinus	0	+26
Palus Epidemiarum	−30	−30
Sinus Aestuum	− 8	+12
Sinus Iridum	−33	+45
Sinus Medii	0	+ 2
Sinus Roris	−45	+53

Mountains

Montes Alpes	Montes Jura
Montes Altai	Montes Pyrenees
Montes Appeninus	Montes Recti
Montes Carpatus	Montes Riphaeus
Montes Caucasus	Montes Spitzbergensis
Montes Cordillera	Montes Teneriffe
Montes Haemus	

Coordinates are not given for mountain ranges most of which border the maria.

Latin names have also been given to rilles, for example: Rima Hyginus. Note as well the Latin term for fault, e.g. Rupes Recta (Straight Wall).

The lunar chart is drawn to a scale of 1:10 million which is another way of saying that if it were magnified 10 million times it would then be the same size as the Moon. It represents the visible hemisphere at mean libration.

The Lunar Chart

Name	Longitude (degrees)	Latitude (degrees)	Name	Longitude (degrees)	Latitude (degrees)
Abenezra	+12	−21	Babbage	−57	+59
Abulfeda	+14	−14	Baco	+19	−51
Adams	+68	−31	Baillaud	+31	+74
Agatharchides	−31	−20	Bailly	−67	−67
Agrippa	+10	+ 4	Baily	+30	+50
Airy	+ 5	−18	Ball	− 8	−36
Albategnius	+ 4	−11	Barocius	+16	−45
Alexander	+14	+40	Barrow	+ 8	+72
Alfraganus	+19	− 5	Beaumont	+28	−18
Alhazen	+72	+16	Beer	− 9	+27
Aliacensis	+ 5	−31	Behaim	+80	−16
Almanon	+15	−17	Bellot	+48	−13
Alpetragius	− 4	−16	Bernouilli	+61	+34
Alphonsus	− 3	−14	Berosus	+69	+33
Anaxagoras	−10	+74	Berzelius	+51	+36
Anaximander	−50	+66	Bessarion	−37	+15
Anaximenes	−44	+72	Bessel	+18	+22
Anděl	+12	−10	Bettinus	−45	−64
Ansagarius	+77	−13	Bianchini	−34	+49
Apianus	+ 8	−27	Biela	+51	−55
Apollonius	+61	+ 4	Billy	−50	−14
Arago	+21	+ 6	Biot	+51	−22
Archimedes	− 4	+30	Birmingham	−11	+64
Archytas	+ 5	+59	Birt	− 9	−22
Argelander	+ 6	−17	Blancanus	−21	−63
Ariadaeus	+17	+ 4	Blanchinus	+ 2	−25
Aristarchus	−48	+24	Bode	− 2	+ 7
Aristoteles	+17	+50	Boguslawsky	+44	−73
Arnold	+36	+67	Bohnenberger	+40	−16
Arzachel	− 2	−18	Bond, G.	+36	+32
Asclepi	+25	−54	Bond, W.	+ 4	+65
Atlas	+44	+46	Bonpland	−17	− 8
Autolycus	+ 1	+31	Borda	+47	−25
Auwers	+17	+15	Boscovich	+11	+ 9
Auzout	+64	+10	Bouguer	−36	+52
Azophi	+13	−22	Boussingault	+54	−70

Name	Longitude (degrees)	Latitude (degrees)	Name	Longitude (degrees)	Latitude (degrees)
Brayley	−37	+21	Cusanus	+70	+72
Breislak	+19	−48	Cuvier	+ 9	−50
Brenner	+38	−40	Cyrillus	+24	−14
Briggs	−69	+26			
Buch	+18	−39	Daguerre	+33	−12
Bullialdus	−22	−21	Damoiseau	−61	− 5
Burckhardt	+57	+31	Daniell	+31	+35
Bürg	+28	+45	Darney	−24	−15
Burnham	+ 7	−14	Darwin	−73	−22
Büsching	+20	−38	Davy	− 8	−12
Byrgius	−66	−25	Dawes	+26	+17
			Debes	+51	+29
Calippus	+10	+39	Dechen	−68	+46
Capella	+35	− 7	Delambre	+17	− 2
Capuanus	−27	−34	De la Rue	+51	+59
Cardanus	−72	+13	Delaunay	+ 2	−22
Carlini	−24	+34	Delisle	−35	+30
Carpenter	−51	+69	Delmotte	+60	+27
Casatus	−30	−72	Deluc	− 3	−55
Cassini	+ 4	+40	Dembowski	+ 7	− 3
Catharina	+23	−18	Democritus	+35	+62
Cauchy	+38	+ 9	Demonax	+58	−78
Cavalerius	−67	+ 5	Descartes	+15	−12
Cavendish	−54	−25	Deseilligny	+20	+21
Cayley	+15	+ 4	Deslandres	− 6	−30
Celsius	+20	−34	Dionysius	+17	+ 3
Censorinus	+32	− 0	Diophantus	−34	+28
Cepheus	+45	+40	Donati	+ 5	−21
Chacornac	+32	+30	Dopplemayer	−41	−29
Chevallier	+51	+45	Dove	+31	−47
Chladni	+ 1	+ 4	Draper	−22	+18
Cichus	−21	−33			
Clairaut	+ 4	−47	Eddington	−72	+21
Clausius	−44	−37	Egede	+11	+48
Clavius	−15	−58	Eimmart	+64	+24
Cleomedes	+55	+27	Encke	−37	+ 5
Colombo	+45	−15	Endymion	+55	+53
Condamine	+27	+53	Epigenes	+ 5	+67
Condorcet	+70	+12	Eratosthenes	−11	+14
Conon	+ 2	+21	Euclides	−29	− 7
Cook	+48	−17	Euctemon	+31	+76
Copernicus	−20	+10	Eudoxus	+16	+44
Crozier	+51	−13	Euler	−29	+23
Crüger	−67	−17			
Curtius	+ 4	−67	Fabricius	+42	−43

Name	Longitude (degrees)	Latitude (degrees)
Faraday	+ 9	−42
Fauth	−20	+ 6
Faye	+ 4	−21
Fermat	+20	−23
Fernelius	+ 5	−38
Feuillée	− 9	+27
Firmicus	+63	+ 7
Flammarion	− 4	− 3
Flamsteed	−44	− 4
Fontana	−57	−16
Fontenelle	−19	+63
Foucault	−40	+50
Fourier	−54	−31
Fracastorius	+33	−21
Fra Mauro	−17	− 6
Franklin	+47	+39
Franz	+40	+16
Fraunhofer	+59	−39
Furnerius	+60	−36
Galilei	−63	+10
Galle	+22	+56
Gambart	−15	+ 1
Gärtner	+34	+59
Gassendi	−40	−18
Gaudibert	+38	−11
Gauricus	−13	−34
Gauss	+78	+36
Gay-Lussac	−21	+14
Geber	+14	−19
Geminus	+57	+34
Gemma Frisius	+13	−34
Gioja	+ 2	+83
Goclenius	+45	−10
Godin	+10	+ 2
Goldschmidt	− 3	+74
Goodacre	+14	−32
Gould	−17	−19
Grimaldi	−68	− 5
Grove	+33	+40
Gruemberger	−11	−67
Gruithuisen	−40	+33
Guericke	−14	−12
Gutenberg	+41	− 8

Name	Longitude (degrees)	Latitude (degrees)
Hagecius	+47	−59
Hahn	+73	+31
Hainzel	−33	−41
Hall	+37	+34
Halley	+ 6	− 8
Hanno	+75	−57
Hansen	+72	+14
Hansteen	−52	−12
Harding	−71	+43
Harpalus	−43	+53
Hase	+62	−29
Heinsius	−18	−39
Heis	−32	+32
Helicon	−23	+40
Hell	− 8	−32
Helmholtz	+61	−67
Heraclitus	+ 5	−49
Hercules	+39	+47
Herigonius	−34	−14
Hermann	−57	− 2
Herodotus	−50	+23
Herschel, C.	−31	+34
Herschel, J.	−41	+62
Herschel, W.	− 2	− 6
Hesiodus	−16	−29
Hevelius	−67	+ 2
Hind	+ 7	− 8
Hippalus	−30	−25
Hipparchus	+ 5	− 5
Holden	+62	−19
Hommel	+34	−55
Hooke	+55	+41
Horrocks	+ 6	− 4
Hortensius	−28	+ 6
Huggins	− 2	−41
Hyginus	+ 6	+ 8
Hypatia	+22	− 4
Ideler	+22	−49
Inghirami	−69	−47
Isidorus	+33	− 8
Jacobi	+11	−57
Jansen	+28	+13
Janssen	+40	−45

Name	Longitude (degrees)	Latitude (degrees)	Name	Longitude (degrees)	Latitude (degrees)
Julius Caesar	+15	+10	Linné	+12	+28
			Littrow	+31	+21
Kaiser	+ 6	−36	Lockyer	+36	−46
Kane	+25	+63	Lohse	+60	−14
Kant	+20	−11	Longomontanus	−22	−50
Kästner	+78	− 6	Lubbock	+42	− 4
Kepler	−38	+ 8	Lubiniezky	−24	−18
Kies	−23	−26	Luther	+24	+33
Kinau	+15	−61	Lyell	+40	+14
Kirch	− 6	+39			
Kircher	−44	−66	Maclaurin	+68	− 2
Kirchhoff	+39	+30	Maclear	+20	+10
Klaproth	−26	−69	McClure	+50	−15
Klein	+ 2	−12	Macrobius	+46	+21
König	−25	−24	Mädler	+30	−11
Krafft	−73	+17	Magelhaens	+44	−12
Krieger	−46	+29	Maginus	− 8	−50
Krusenstern	+ 6	−26	Main	+10	+81
			Mairan	−43	+42
Lacaille	+ 1	−24	Mallet	+54	−45
Lade	+10	− 1	Manilius	+ 9	+14
Lagalla	−23	−44	Manners	+20	+ 4
Lagrange	−73	−33	Manzinus	+27	−68
Lahire	−25	+28	Maraldi	+35	+19
Lalande	− 9	− 4	Marinus	+76	−39
Lambert	−21	+26	Marius	−51	+12
Lamont	+23	+ 5	Markov	−62	+53
Lansberg	−27	0	Maskelyne	+30	+ 2
Langrenus	+61	− 9	Mason	+30	+42
Lapeyrouse	+76	−10	Maupertius	−28	+49
Lassell	− 8	−15	Maurolycus	+14	−41
Lavoisier	−80	+38	Maury	+40	+37
Lee	−40	−31	Mayer, C.	+17	+63
Legendre	+70	−29	Mayer, T.	−29	+16
Lehmann	−56	−40	Mee	−35	−43
Lemonnier	+30	+26	Menelaus	+16	+16
Letronne	−42	−10	Mercurius	+66	+45
Leverrier	−21	+40	Mersenius	−50	−22
Lexell	− 4	−36	Messala	+60	+39
Licetus	+ 7	−47	Messier	+47	− 2
Lichtenberg	−67	+32	Messier, A.	+47	− 2
Lick	+52	+13	Metius	+44	−40
Liebig	−48	−24	Meton	+21	+73
Lilius	+ 6	−54	Milichius	−30	+10
Lindenau	+25	−32	Miller	+ 1	−39

Name	Longitude (degrees)	Latitude (degrees)
Mitchell	+20	+49
Moigno	+28	+66
Monge	+47	−19
Moretus	− 6	−70
Mösting	+ 6	− 1
Mösting, A.	− 5	− 3
Murchison	0	+ 5
Mutus	+31	−64
Nasireddin	0	−41
Neander	+40	−31
Nearch	+39	−58
Neison	+23	+67
Neper	+83	+ 9
Newcomb	+44	+29
Newton	−15	−76
Nicolai	+27	−43
Nicollet	−12	−22
Nonius	+ 4	−35
Oenopides	−64	+57
Oersted	+47	+43
Oken	+76	−44
Olbers	−76	+ 7
Opelt	−18	−16
Oppolzer	0	− 1
Orontius	− 4	−41
Pallas	− 2	+ 5
Palmieri	−48	−29
Pascal	−50	+71
Parrot	+ 3	−15
Parry	−16	− 8
Pierce	+53	+18
Pentland	+11	−65
Petavius	+60	−25
Petermann	+66	+74
Philolaus	−32	+72
Phocylides	−57	−53
Piazzi	−68	−36
Piazzi Smyth	− 3	+42
Picard	+54	+14
Piccolomini	+32	−30
Pico	− 9	+46
Pictet	− 8	−44

Name	Longitude (degrees)	Latitude (degrees)
Pitatus	−14	−30
Pitiscus	+31	−50
Piton	− 1	+41
Plana	+28	+41
Plato	− 9	+51
Playfair	+ 8	−23
Plinius	+23	+15
Plutarch	+79	+24
Poisson	+10	−31
Polybius	+25	−22
Pons	+21	−25
Pontanus	+14	−28
Pontécoulant	+66	−59
Posidonius	+29	+32
Prinz	−44	+26
Proclus	+47	+16
Proctor	− 6	−46
Protagoras	+ 7	+56
Ptolemaeus	− 3	−10
Purbach	− 2	−25
Pythagoras	−62	+63
Pytheas	−21	+21
Rabbi Levi	+23	−35
Ramsden	−32	−33
Reaumur	+ 1	− 2
Regiomontanus	− 1	−28
Reichenbach	+48	−30
Reimarus	+60	−47
Reiner	−55	+ 6
Reiner, Ö	−58	+ 8
Reinhold	−23	+ 3
Repsold	−78	+51
Rhaeticus	+ 5	0
Rheita	+48	−37
Riccioli	−74	− 3
Riccius	+26	−37
Ritchey	+ 8	−11
Ritter	+19	+ 2
Rocca	−75	−13
Römer	+36	+25
Rosenberger	+42	−55
Ross	+22	+11
Rosse	+35	−18
Rothmann	+28	−31

Name	Longitude (degrees)	Latitude (degrees)	Name	Longitude (degrees)	Latitude (degrees)
Rumker	−58	+41	Thales	+50	+62
Rutherfurd	−12	−61	Theaetetus	+ 6	+37
			Thebit	+ 4	−22
Sabine	+20	+ 1	Theon Junior	+16	− 2
Sacrobosco	+16	−23	Theon Senior	+15	− 1
Santbech	+44	−21	Theophilus	+26	−11
Sasserides	−10	−39	Timocharis	−13	+27
Saunder	+ 9	− 4	Tisserand	+48	+21
Saussure	− 5	−43	Torricelli	+28	− 5
Scheiner	−28	−60	Tralles	+53	+28
Schiaparelli	−59	+23	Triesnecker	+ 3	+ 4
Schickard	−56	−44	Tycho	−11	−45
Schiller	−40	−52			
Schluter	−88	− 6	Ukert	+ 1	+ 8
Schmidt	+19	0	Ulugh Beigh	−81	+33
Schomberger	+25	−76			
Schröter	− 7	+ 3	Vasco da Gama	−84	+14
Schumacher	+60	+42	Vega	+63	−45
Scoresby	+14	+78	Vendelinus	+62	−16
Scott	+90	−86	Vieta	−57	−29
Secchi	+43	+ 2	Vitello	−37	−30
Segner	−48	−59	Vitruvius	+31	+17
Seleucus	−67	+21	Vlacq	+38	−53
Seneca	+81	+29	Vogel	+ 6	−15
Sharp	−40	+46			
Sheepshanks	+17	+59	Wallace	− 9	+20
Shuckburgh	+53	+43	Walter	+ 1	−33
Simpelius	+15	−73	Wargentin	−61	−50
Sinas	+31	+ 9	Watt	+48	−49
Sirsalis	−73	−22	Webb	+60	− 1
Snellius	+55	−29	Weinek	+37	−27
Sosigenes	+17	+ 8	Weiss	−20	−32
South	−50	+57	Werner	+ 3	−28
Stadius	−14	+11	Wichmann	−38	− 8
Steinheil	+46	−48	Wilhelm	−21	−43
Stevinus	+54	−33	Wilkins	+20	−30
Stiborius	+32	−34	Williams	+37	+42
Stöfler	+ 5	−41	Wilson	−43	−69
Strabo	+54	+62	Wolf	−17	−23
Street	−11	−46	Wollaston	−47	+31
Struve, O.	−75	+29	Wrottesley	+57	−24
			Wurzelbauer	−16	−34
Tacitus	+19	−16			
Taruntius	+46	+ 5	Xenophanes	−79	+57
Taylor	+16	− 5			

Name	Longitude (degrees)	Latitude (degrees)	Name	Longitude (degrees)	Latitude (degrees)
Zach	+ 5	−61	Zöllner	+19	− 8
Zagut	+22	−32	Zucchius	−50	−61
Zeno	+74	+45	Zupus	−53	−17

Bibliography

LUNAR researches are pouring out results at such a pace that it is impossible for anyone to remain up to date without almost constant revision. Books take longer to prepare than scientific journals, so the latter are more current with the latest trends and discoveries. Many large technical libraries subscribe to the following:

> *Nature* (published every Saturday).
> *Astronomical Journal.*
> *Icarus.*
> *Sky and Telescope* (published each month).
> *Journal of Geophysical Research.*
> *Astrophysical Journal.*
> *Journal of the British Astronomical Association.*

The above are a small selection from a large number that are kept in the bigger libraries.

It is more difficult to recommend books because of the delays between writing and printing. Good coverage of most aspects other than the recent space probe discoveries may be obtained from the following:

The Moon, Edited by Z. KOPAL and Z. K. MIKHAILOV, Academic Press, 1962.
Physics and Astronomy of the Moon, Editor Z. KOPAL, Academic Press, 1962.
Structure of the Moon's Surface, By G. FIELDER, Pergamon Press, 1961.
The Moon: A Russian View, Editor A. V. MARKOV, University of Chicago Press, 1962.
Photographic Atlas of the Moon, By Z. KOPAL, T. W. RACKHAM and J. KLEPESTA, Academic Press, 1965.

More specialized are:

The Lunar Surface Layer, By J. W. SALISBURY and P. E. GLASER, Academic Press, 1964.
Lunar Missions and Explorations, Edited by C. T. LEONDES and R. W. VANCE, John Wiley & Sons, 1964.

An Introduction to the Study of the Moon, by Z. KOPAL, D. Reidel Publishing Co., 1966.

Specific references relevant to the contents of Chapters 4 – 7 inclusive are given below.

ALTER, D., Suspected partial obscuration of the floor of Alphonsus, *Publications Astronomical Society of the Pacific*, Vol. 69, No. 158, 1957.

COSTAIN, C. H., ELSMORE, B. and WHITFIELD, G. R., Radio observations of a lunar occultation of the Crab Nebula, *Monthly Notices of Royal Astronomical Society*, Vol. 116, 1956.

ELSMORE, B. and WHITFIELD, G. R., The lunar occultation of a radio star and the derivation of an upper limit for the density of the lunar atmosphere, *Nature*, Vol. 176, Sept. 1955.

EVANS, J. V., Radio echo studies of the Moon, in *Physics and Astronomy of the Moon*, Ed. Z. KOPAL, Academic Press, 1962.

GOLD, T., Dust on the Moon, in *Vistas in Astronautics*, Vol. 2, July 1958.

GOLD, T., Processes on the lunar surface, in *The Moon*, I.A.U. Symposium No. 14. Ed. Z. KOPAL and Z. K. MIKHAILOV, Academic Press, 1960.

GOUDAS, C. L., KOPAL, Z. and KOPAL, Z., The shape of the Moon as deduced from the orbiter determination of its gravitational field, Boeing Scientific Research Labs. Document No. D1–82–0570, Oct. 1966.

GREEN, J., The geosciences applied to lunar exploration, in *The Moon*, I.A.U. Symposium No. 14, Ed. Z. KOPAL and Z. K. MIKHAILOV, Academic Press, 1960.

HAPKE, B. W., Photometric and other laboratory studies relating to the lunar surface, in *The Lunar Surface Layer*, Ed. J. W. SALISBURY and P. E. GLASER, Academic Press, 1964.

KOSYREV, N. A., Observation of a volcanic process on the Moon, *Sky and Telescope*, Vol. 18, No. 184, 1959.

KOSYREV, N. A., Spectrographic proofs for the existence of volcanic processes on the Moon, in *The Moon*, I.A.U. Symposium No. 14, Ed. Z. KOPAL and Z. K. MIKHAILOV, Academic Press, 1960.

KOSYREV, N. A., Volcanic phenomena on the Moon, *Nature*, Vol. 198, pp. 979–80, 1963.

KUIPER, G. P., Rangers 7–9, *Sky and Telescope*, Vol. 29, No. 5, May 1965.

KUIPER, G. P., STROM, R. G. and LE POOLE, R. S., Interpretation of the Ranger records, in NASA Technical Report No. 32–800, Ranger VIII and IX, Jet Propulsion Laboratory, March 1966.

LINK, F. Theorie photometrique des eclipses de la Lune, *Bulletin Astronomique*, Vol. 8, No. 77, 1933.

LIPSKY, Y. N., Zond 3 photographs of the Moon's far side, *Sky and Telescope*, Vol. 30, No. 6, Dec. 1965.

LYOT, B. and DOLLFUS, A., Recherche d'une atmosphere au voisinage de la Lune, *Comptes Rendus*, Paris Academy Sciences, Vol. 229, pp. 1277–80, 1949.

MARKOV, A. V., BARABASHEV, N. P., SHARONOV, V. V., SYTINSKAYA, N. N. *et al.*, in *The Moon: a Russian View*, Ed. A. V. MARKOV, translation Ed. F. J. HEYDEN, University of Chicago Press, 1962.

MEYER, D. L. and RUFFIN, B. W., *Icarus*, Vol. 4, pp. 513, Academic Press, 1965.

ÖPIK, E. J., The lunar atmosphere, *Planetary and Space Sciences*, Vol. 9, May 1962.

SAARI, J. M. and SHORTHILL, R. W., Hot spots on the Moon, *Sky and Telescope*, Vol. 31, No. 6, June 1966.

SAARI, J. M. and SHORTHILL, R. W., Review of lunar infrared observations, Boeing Scientific Research Labs. Document No. D1–82–0586, Dec. 1966.

SINGER, S. F. and WALKER, E. H., Electrostatic dust transport on the lunar surface, *Icarus*, Vol. 1, No. 2, Sept. 1962.

UREY, H. C., Origin and history of the Moon, in *Physics and Astronomy of the Moon*, Ed. Z. KOPAL, Academic Press, 1962.

WATSON, K., MURRAY, B. C. and BROWN, H., On the possible presence of ice on the Moon, *Journal of Geophysical Research*, Vol. 66, pp. 1598–1600, 1961.

WHIPPLE, F. L., On the lunar dust layer, in *Vistas in Astronautics*, Vol. 2, Pergamon Press, 1959.

Notes Added in Proof

1. American Lunar Orbiters 4 and 5, launched 4th May and 1st August, 1967, have completed the task of photographing the far side of the Moon. See also pp. 129 and 161.

2. Surveyor 5, now resting on the lunar surface since 11th September, 1967, contains a miniature chemical laboratory for testing the nature of the lunar soil.

3. The "digger" on Surveyor 3 sampled lunar soil 72 miles S.E. of the crater Lansberg (21st April 1967) and found it to behave like "coarse, damp beach sand".

4. American Lunar Orbiters 4 and 5 (see p. 161), have photographed all of the far side of the Moon. The 24-inch system showed objects down to 200 feet across. To achieve this, orbital distances were increased as follows: Orbiter 4: apolune 3844 miles, perilune 1623 miles; Orbiter 5: apolune 3740 miles, perilune 122 miles.

Index

Note: No attempt has been made to index craters and named formations; this information is to be found on pages 164–72 inclusive.